GCSE AQA
Additional Science
Foundation Revision Guide

This book is for anyone doing **GCSE AQA Additional Science** at foundation level.
It covers everything you'll need for your year 11 exams.

GCSE Science is all about **understanding how science works**.
And not only that — understanding it well enough to be able to **question**
what you hear on TV and read in the papers.

But you can't do that without a fair chunk of **background knowledge**. Hmm, tricky.

Happily this CGP book includes all the **science facts** you need to learn,
and shows you how they work in the **real world**. And in true CGP style,
we've explained it all as **clearly and concisely** as possible.

It's also got some daft bits in to try and make the whole
experience at least vaguely entertaining for you.

<u>What CGP is all about</u>

Our sole aim here at CGP is to produce the highest
quality books — carefully written, immaculately presented
and dangerously close to being funny.

Then we work our socks off to get them
out to you — at the cheapest possible prices.

Contents

Published by CGP

From original material by Richard Parsons.

Editors:
Charlotte Burrows, Katherine Craig, Helena Hayes, Felicity Inkpen,
Rosie McCurrie, Jane Sawers, Sarah Williams.

ISBN: 978 1 84762 759 9

With thanks to Philip Dobson, Mary Falkner, Ian Francis, Rosie McCurrie, Philip Rushworth
and Karen Wells for the proofreading.
With thanks to Jan Greenway, Laura Jakubowski and Laura Stoney for the copyright research.

Data used to construct stopping distance diagram on page 79 from the Highway Code. ©
Crown Copyright re-produced under the terms of the Click-Use licence.

Groovy website: www.cgpbooks.co.uk

Printed by Elanders Ltd, Newcastle upon Tyne.
Jolly bits of clipart from CorelDRAW®

The Exams

This stuff is as dull as dishwater, but you really need to <u>know what you're in for</u>...

Make Sure You Know Which Exam Route You're Doing

1) You'll have to do exams that test your <u>knowledge of Biology, Chemistry and Physics</u>.

2) You <u>also</u> need to know about <u>How Science Works</u>. There's a whole section about it to help you — see pages 2-10. Make sure you understand it <u>all</u> before the exams.

3) You also have to do a <u>Controlled Assessment</u> (also known as an 'ISA') — it's a bit like a <u>coursework exam</u>. See page 11 for more.

4) There are <u>two different exam routes</u> you can take:

ROUTE 1	WHAT YOU NEED TO REVISE FROM THIS BOOK
• Unit 1 exam — Biology 2	• Sections B2a and B2b
• Unit 2 exam — Chemistry 2	• Sections C2a and C2b
• Unit 3 exam — Physics 2	• Sections P2a and P2b
• Controlled Assessment (ISA)	• How Science Works pages 2-11

OR

ROUTE 2	WHAT YOU NEED TO REVISE FROM THIS BOOK
• Unit 5 exam — 1st half of Biology 2, 1st half of Chemistry 2, 1st half of Physics 2	• Sections B2a, C2a and P2a
• Unit 6 exam — 2nd half of Biology 2, 2nd half of Chemistry 2, 2nd half of Physics 2	• Sections B2b, C2b and P2b
• Controlled Assessment (ISA)	• How Science Works pages 2-11

5) If you don't know which route you're doing <u>ASK YOUR TEACHER</u>, so you revise the <u>RIGHT STUFF</u> for the <u>RIGHT EXAM</u>.

Top Tips for Top Marks in the Exam

1) For some of the <u>long answer questions</u> you'll be marked on your <u>spelling</u>, <u>punctuation</u> and <u>grammar</u>. Remember to write in <u>full sentences</u> and check your work at the end of the exam.

2) <u>Double-check</u> your answer if you've had to <u>calculate</u> something. Write down all your <u>working out</u> and don't forget to include the <u>units</u> either.

3) The examiners expect you to be able to <u>use your knowledge</u> to answer questions about <u>unfamiliar things</u>, e.g. use your knowledge of wave refraction to answer questions about glasses lenses. Don't panic — you should be able to <u>work it out</u> using <u>what you've learnt about the topic</u>.

Exam routes — simpler than bus routes...

Revising for exams is about as exciting as <u>watching paint dry</u>, but it's the only way you'll get <u>good marks</u>. Try to spend a little more time revising the topics you find hard. And make sure you know <u>what you should be revising for each exam</u> — you'll feel a right idiot if you learn the wrong stuff.

How Science Works

The Scientific Process

For your <u>exams</u> and your <u>controlled assessment</u>, you need to know about how the world of science works.

Science is All About Testing Hypotheses

| Scientists make an observation. |

1) Scientists <u>OBSERVE</u> (look at) something they don't understand, e.g. an illness.
2) They come up with a <u>possible explanation</u> for what they've observed.
3) This explanation is called a <u>HYPOTHESIS</u>.

| They test their hypothesis. |

4) Next, they test whether the hypothesis is <u>right or not</u>.
5) They do this by making a <u>PREDICTION</u> — a statement based on the hypothesis that can be tested.
6) They then <u>TEST</u> this prediction by carrying out <u>experiments</u>.
7) If their prediction is <u>right</u>, this is <u>EVIDENCE</u> that their <u>hypothesis might be right</u> too.

| Other scientists test the explanation too. |

8) Other scientists carry out <u>more experiments</u> to test the hypothesis.
9) Sometimes these scientists will find <u>more evidence</u> that the <u>hypothesis is RIGHT</u>.
10) Sometimes they'll find <u>evidence</u> that shows the <u>hypothesis is WRONG</u>.

| The explanation is accepted or rejected. |

11) If <u>all the evidence</u> that's been found <u>supports</u> the <u>hypothesis</u>, it becomes an <u>ACCEPTED THEORY</u> and goes into <u>textbooks</u> for people to learn.
12) If the <u>evidence</u> shows that the hypothesis is <u>wrong</u>, scientists must:
   - <u>Change the hypothesis</u>, OR
   - Come up with a <u>new hypothesis</u>.

Hundreds of years ago, we thought demons caused illness.

Then we thought it was caused by 'bad blood' (and treated it with leeches).

Now we know most illnesses are due to microorganisms.

You expect me to believe that — then show me the evidence...

If scientists think something is true, they need to produce evidence to convince others — it's all part of <u>testing a hypothesis</u>. Along the way some hypotheses will be <u>disproved</u> (shown not to be true).

Your Data's Got To be Good

Evidence is the key to science — but not all evidence is good...

Lab Experiments and Studies Are Better Than Rumour

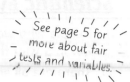

See page 5 for more about fair tests and variables.

1) <u>Laboratory experiments</u> are <u>great</u>. A lab is the easiest place to <u>control the variables</u> in your experiment. This makes it easier to carry out a <u>FAIR TEST</u>.

2) For things that you <u>can't study in a lab</u> (e.g. climate) you carry out <u>scientific studies</u>. In studies, you control as many of the variables as possible.

3) Old wives' tales and rumours are <u>NOT scientific</u>. Without any evidence, they're just <u>opinions</u>.

The Bigger the Sample Size the Better

1) Sample size is <u>how many things you test</u> in an experiment or study, e.g. 500 people or 20 types of metal.

2) The <u>bigger</u> the sample size the <u>better</u> — to <u>reduce</u> the chance of any <u>weird results</u>.

3) But scientists have to be <u>realistic</u> when choosing how big their sample should be. E.g. if you were studying how lifestyle affects weight it'd be great to study everyone in the UK (a huge sample), but it'd take ages and cost loads.

Evidence Needs to be Reliable

<u>Reliable evidence</u> comes from <u>experiments</u> that give the <u>same data</u>:

- each time the experiment is <u>repeated</u>
- each time the experiment is <u>reproduced</u> (copied) by <u>other scientists</u>.

RELIABLE means that the data can be <u>repeated, and reproduced by others</u>.

<u>EXAMPLE:</u> In 1998, a scientist claimed that he'd found a link between the <u>MMR vaccine</u> (for measles, mumps and rubella) and <u>autism</u>. But other scientists <u>couldn't</u> get the <u>same results</u> — they <u>weren't reliable</u>.

Evidence Also Needs to Be Valid

VALID means that the data is <u>reliable</u> AND <u>answers the original question</u>.

<u>EXAMPLE: DO POWER LINES CAUSE CANCER?</u>
- Some studies have found that in areas where there were <u>power lines</u>, <u>more children</u> had <u>cancer</u>.
- This evidence is <u>NOT enough</u> to say that the power lines <u>CAUSE</u> cancer. Other explanations might be possible, e.g. power lines are often near <u>busy roads</u>, so the areas tested could contain <u>different levels</u> of <u>pollution</u> from traffic.
- So these studies <u>don't</u> show a <u>definite link</u> and so <u>don't answer the original question</u>.

RRRR — Remember, Reliable means Repeatable and Reproducible...

So. Now you know loads about <u>evidence</u>. The fun doesn't stop here though — there's more on the next page.

Bias and Issues Created by Science

It isn't all fun and games in the world of science — there are some problems...

Scientific Evidence can be Biased

1) People who want to make a point can sometimes present data in a biased way —
   i.e. in a way that's meant to affect how other people think.

2) There are all sorts of reasons why people might want to do this — for example...

   - Scientists might want to keep the company that's paying for the research happy.
     (If the company's not happy they might not pay for any more research.)
   - Governments might want to persuade voters to vote for them.
   - Companies might want to make their products sound better.

Scientific Developments are Great, but they can Raise Issues

Scientific knowledge increases by doing experiments. This knowledge leads to scientific developments,
e.g. new technology or new advice. These developments can create issues though. For example:

Economic (money) issues:

Governments can't always afford to do
things scientists recommend, e.g. spend
money on green energy sources.

Social (people) issues:

Decisions based on scientific evidence
affect people — e.g. should alcohol be
banned (to prevent health problems)?

Ethical (moral) issues:

There are a lot of things science has made
possible, but should we do them? E.g. clone
humans, develop better nuclear weapons.

Environmental issues:

Nuclear power helps us produce more
energy — but some people think it causes
too many environmental problems.

Some Questions are Unanswered by Science — Some are Unanswerable

1) At the moment scientists don't agree on some things, e.g. what the universe is made of.

2) This is because there isn't enough reliable and valid evidence.

3) But eventually, we probably will be able to answer these questions once and for all.

4) All we need is more evidence.

5) But the question of whether something is ethically right or wrong can't ever be answered
   by more experiments. There is no "right" or "wrong" answer.

6) The best we can do is make a decision that most people are more or less happy to live by.

CGP make the best revision guides — nope, no bias here...

Spotting biased evidence isn't the easiest thing in the world — ask yourself, 'Will the scientist gain something
(or lose something)?' If they might it's possible that the evidence could be biased.

Designing Investigations

You need to know a shed load about <u>investigations</u> for your <u>controlled assessment</u> and <u>all your exams</u>. Investigations include <u>experiments</u> and <u>studies</u>. The next six pages take you from start to finish. Enjoy.

Investigations Produce Evidence to Support or Disprove a Hypothesis

1) When scientists <u>observe</u> something they come up with a <u>hypothesis</u> to explain it (see page 2).

2) To decide whether a hypothesis is correct or not you need to do an <u>investigation</u> to <u>gather some evidence</u>.

3) The first step is to use the hypothesis to come up with a <u>prediction</u> — a statement about what you <u>think will happen</u> that you can <u>test</u>.

4) For example, if your <u>hypothesis</u> is:

> "Spots are caused by picking your nose too much."

Then your <u>prediction</u> might be:

> "People who pick their nose more often will have more spots."

Sometimes a hypothesis and a prediction are the same thing.

5) Investigations are used to see if there are <u>patterns</u> or <u>relationships between two variables</u> (see below).

6) The investigation has to be a <u>FAIR TEST</u> to make sure the evidence is <u>reliable</u> and <u>valid</u>...

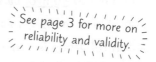

See page 3 for more on reliability and validity.

To Make an Investigation a Fair Test You Have to Control the Variables

Investigations that you plan should always be a <u>fair test</u>.

1) In a lab experiment you usually <u>change one thing</u> (a variable) and <u>measure</u> how it affects <u>another thing</u> (another variable).

> EXAMPLE: you might change only the angle of a slope and measure how it affects the time taken for a toy car to travel down it.

2) <u>Everything else</u> that could affect the results needs to <u>stay the same</u>. Then you know that the thing you're <u>changing</u> is the <u>only</u> thing that's affecting the results.

> EXAMPLE continued: you need to keep the slope length the same. If you don't, you won't know if any change in the time taken is caused by the change in angle, or the change in length.

3) The variable that you <u>CHANGE</u> is called the <u>INDEPENDENT</u> variable.

4) The variable that's <u>MEASURED</u> is called the <u>DEPENDENT</u> variable.

5) The variables that you <u>keep the same</u> are called <u>control</u> variables.

> EXAMPLE continued:
> Independent variable = angle of slope
> Dependent variable = time taken
> Control variable = length of slope

Designing Investigations

Trial Runs Help Figure out the Range and Interval of Variable Values

1) A trial run is a quick version of your experiment.

2) Trial runs help you work out whether your plan is right or not — you might decide to make some changes after trying out your method.

3) They're used to figure out the range of values (the highest and lowest value) for the variable you're changing (the independent variable).

4) And they're used to figure out the interval (gaps) between the values too.

Slope example from previous page continued:

- You might do trial runs at 20, 40, 60 and 80°. If the time taken is too short to accurately measure at 80°, you might narrow the range to 20-60°.

- If using 20° intervals gives you a big change in time taken you might decide to use 10° intervals, e.g. 20, 30, 40, 50°...

5) Trial runs can also help you figure out how many times the experiment has to be repeated to get reliable results. E.g. if you repeat it three times and the results are all similar, then three repeats is enough.

It Can Be Hard to Control the Variables in a Study

1) You have to control all the variables in a study or it won't be a fair test (just like in a lab experiment).

2) Sometimes though, this is really hard — so you have to use a control group to help.

3) A control group is group of whatever you're studying (e.g. plants) that's kept under the same conditions as the group in the experiment. However, the control group doesn't have anything done to it.

EXAMPLE:

- If you're studying the effect of pesticides (pest killer) on plant growth, pesticide is put on one field but not another field (the control field).

- Both fields contain the same plants and get the same weather conditions.

- The control field is there so that you can check it's the pesticide causing the results — not the weather.

Investigations Can be Hazardous

1) A hazard is something that could cause harm.

2) Hazards include things like microorganisms (e.g. bacteria), chemicals, electricity and fire.

3) Scientists need to manage the risk of hazards by doing things to reduce them. For example:

- If you're using a Bunsen burner, stand it on a heat-proof mat.
- This will reduce the risk of starting a fire.

You won't get a trial run at the exam, so get learnin'...

All this info needs to be firmly lodged in your memory. Learn the names of the different variables — if you remember that the variable you chaNge is called the iNdependent variable, you can figure out the other ones.

Collecting Data

It's good if you can design an investigation that people will praise for years to come.
But you'll also need to get your hands mucky and <u>collect some data</u>.

Your Data Should be as Reliable, Accurate and Precise as Possible

1) To make your results more reliable, you should repeat each reading at least <u>three</u> times.
   Then you can calculate the <u>mean</u> (average) — see next page.

2) Checking your results match with <u>secondary sources</u>
   (e.g. other studies) also makes your data more reliable.

3) Your data also needs to be <u>ACCURATE</u>. Accurate results
   are those that are <u>really close</u> to the <u>true answer</u>.

4) Your data also needs to be <u>PRECISE</u>. Precise results
   are ones that are <u>really similar</u> to the <u>mean</u>.

Repeat	Data set 1	Data set 2
1	12	11
2	14	18
3	13	10
Mean	13	13

Data set 1 is more precise
than data set 2.

The Equipment Used has to be Right for the Job

1) You need to make sure you choose the <u>right equipment</u>.

2) For example, the measuring equipment you use has to be able to <u>accurately</u> measure the chemicals
   you're using. If you need to measure out 11 ml of a liquid, use a measuring cylinder that can
   measure to 1 ml, not 5 or 10 ml.

3) The <u>smallest change</u> a measuring instrument can <u>detect</u> is called its <u>RESOLUTION</u>.
   E.g. some mass balances have a resolution of 1 g, some have a resolution of 0.1 g.

4) Equipment needs to be <u>CALIBRATED</u> (set up properly) so that your data is <u>more accurate</u>.
   E.g. mass balances need to be set to zero before you start weighing things.

Errors can Pop Up if You're Not Careful

1) The results of your experiment will always <u>vary a bit</u>.

2) Sometimes, errors will be made. If the <u>same error</u> is made every time, it's called a <u>SYSTEMATIC ERROR</u>.

3) If a systematic error is caused by using <u>equipment</u> that <u>isn't calibrated properly</u> it's called a <u>ZERO ERROR</u>.

Errors can Affect Your Results

1) Sometimes you get a result that <u>doesn't seem to fit in</u>
   with the rest at all.

2) These results are called <u>ANOMALOUS RESULTS</u>.

3) You should investigate them and try to <u>work out what happened</u>.

4) If you can work out what happened (e.g. you measured something
   wrong) you can <u>ignore</u> them when processing your results.

Park	Number of pigeons	Number of crazy tramps
A	28	1
B	42	2
C	1127	0

Anomalous result

Zero error — sounds like a Bruce Willis film...

Weirdly, data can be really <u>precise</u> but <u>not very accurate</u>, e.g. a fancy piece of lab equipment might give results
that are precise, but if it's not calibrated properly those results won't be accurate.

Processing and Presenting Data

The fun doesn't stop once you've collected your data — it then needs to be <u>processed</u> and <u>presented</u>...

Data Needs to be Organised

1) Data that's been collected needs to be <u>organised</u> so it can be processed later on.

2) <u>Tables</u> are dead useful for <u>organising data</u>.

3) You should always make sure that <u>each column</u> has a <u>heading</u> and that you've included the <u>units</u>.

Test tube	Repeat 1 (ml)	Repeat 2 (ml)	Repeat 3 (ml)
A	28	37	32
B	47	51	60
C	68	72	70

You Might Have to Process Your Data

1) When you've done repeats of an experiment you should always calculate the <u>MEAN</u> (average).

2) To calculate the mean <u>ADD TOGETHER</u> all the data values. Then <u>DIVIDE</u> by the total number of data values.

3) You might also need to calculate the <u>RANGE</u> (how spread out the data is).

4) To do this find the <u>LARGEST</u> number and <u>SUBTRACT</u> the <u>SMALLEST</u> number from it.

Ignore anomalous results when calculating these.

<u>EXAMPLE:</u>

Test tube	Repeat 1 (g)	Repeat 2 (g)	Repeat 3 (g)	Mean (g)	Range (g)
A	28	37	32	(28 + 37 + 32) ÷ 3 = 32.3	37 – 28 = 9
B	47	51	60	(47 + 51 + 60) ÷ 3 = 52.7	60 – 47 = 13
C	68	72	70	(68 + 72 + 70) ÷ 3 = 70.0	72 – 68 = 4

If Your Data Comes in Categories, Present it in a Bar Chart

1) If the independent variable comes in <u>clear categories</u> (e.g. blood types, metals) you should use a <u>bar chart</u> to display the data.

2) There are some <u>golden rules</u> you need to follow for <u>drawing</u> bar charts:

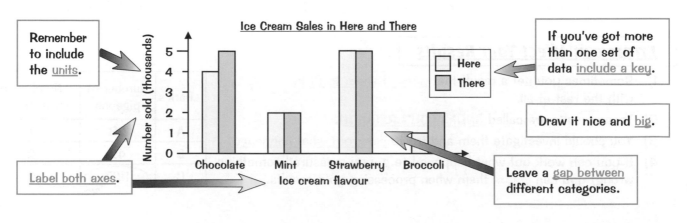

Remember to include the <u>units</u>.

<u>Label both axes</u>.

If you've got more than one set of data <u>include a key</u>.

Draw it nice and <u>big</u>.

Leave a <u>gap between</u> different categories.

Here's a tip from me — never present data as a Mother's Day gift...

Examiners are a bit picky when it comes to bar charts — if you don't draw them properly they won't be happy. Also, <u>double check</u> any mean or range <u>calculations</u> you do, just to be sure you've got them right.

Presenting Data

Scientists just <u>love</u> presenting data as <u>line graphs</u> (weirdos)...

If Your Data Covers a Range of Values, Plot a Line Graph

If the independent variable can have any value within a range (e.g. length, volume, temperature) you should use a <u>line graph</u> to display the data.

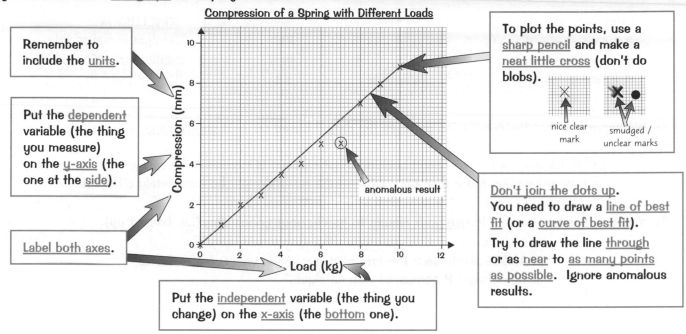

Remember to include the <u>units</u>.

Put the <u>dependent</u> variable (the thing you measure) on the <u>y-axis</u> (the one at the <u>side</u>).

<u>Label both axes</u>.

Put the <u>independent</u> variable (the thing you change) on the <u>x-axis</u> (the <u>bottom</u> one).

To plot the points, use a <u>sharp pencil</u> and make a <u>neat little cross</u> (don't do blobs).

nice clear mark

smudged / unclear marks

anomalous result

<u>Don't join the dots up</u>. You need to draw a <u>line of best fit</u> (or a <u>curve of best fit</u>).

Try to draw the line <u>through</u> or as <u>near</u> to <u>as many points as possible</u>. Ignore anomalous results.

Line Graphs Can Show Patterns in Data

1) Line graphs are used to <u>show the relationship</u> between two variables (just like other graphs).

2) The relationship between two variables is called a <u>CORRELATION</u>:

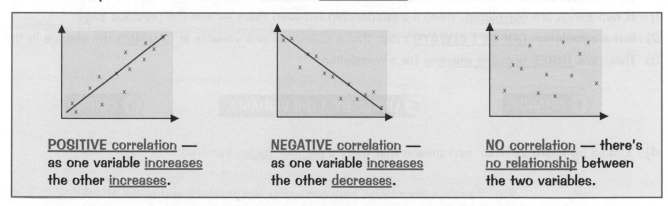

<u>POSITIVE</u> correlation — as one variable <u>increases</u> the other <u>increases</u>.

<u>NEGATIVE</u> correlation — as one variable <u>increases</u> the other <u>decreases</u>.

<u>NO</u> correlation — there's <u>no relationship</u> between the two variables.

3) You need to be able to describe the following patterns on line graphs too:

<u>LINEAR</u> — the graph is a <u>straight line</u>.

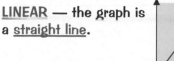

<u>DIRECTLY PROPORTIONAL</u> — the graph is a <u>straight line</u> where both variables increase (or decrease) in the <u>same ratio</u>.

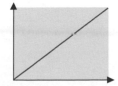

There's a positive correlation between revision and boredom...

...but there's also a positive correlation between <u>revision</u> and getting a <u>better mark in the exam</u>. Cover the page and write down the <u>six things</u> you need to remember when <u>drawing line graphs</u>. No sneaky peeking either — I saw you.

Drawing Conclusions

Congratulations — you've made it to the <u>final step</u> of an investigation — <u>drawing conclusions</u>.

You Can Only Conclude What the Data Shows and NO MORE

1) To come to a conclusion, <u>look at your data</u> and <u>say what pattern you see</u>.

> EXAMPLE: The table on the right shows the rate of a reaction with two different catalysts.
>
> | Catalyst | Rate of reaction (cm^3/s) |
> |----------|------------------------------|
> | A | 13.5 |
> | B | 19.5 |
> | No catalyst | 5.5 |
>
> <u>CONCLUSION</u>: Catalyst <u>B</u> makes <u>this reaction</u> go faster than catalyst A.

2) It's important that the conclusion <u>matches the data</u> it based on — it <u>shouldn't go any further</u>.

> EXAMPLE continued: You <u>can't</u> conclude that catalyst B increases the rate of <u>any other reaction</u> more than catalyst A — the results might be completely different.

3) You also need to be able to <u>use your results</u> to <u>justify your conclusion</u> (i.e. back it up).

> EXAMPLE continued: The rate of this reaction was 6 cm^3/s faster using catalyst B compared with catalyst A.

Correlation DOESN'T Always Mean Cause

1) If two things are <u>correlated</u>, there's a relationship between them — see the previous page.

2) But a correlation <u>DOESN'T ALWAYS</u> mean that a change in one variable is <u>CAUSING</u> the change in the other.

3) There are <u>THREE possible reasons</u> for a correlation:

 CHANCE  LINKED BY A 3rd VARIABLE   CAUSE

4) 'Linked by a 3rd variable' just means that there's <u>another factor</u> involved.

> E.g. there's a correlation between water temperature and shark attacks. They're linked by a <u>third variable</u> — the number of people swimming (more people swim when the water's hotter, which means you get more shark attacks).

I conclude that this page is a bit dull...

In the exams you could be given a <u>conclusion</u> and asked <u>whether some data supports it</u> — so make sure you understand <u>how far conclusions can go</u>.

Controlled Assessment (ISA)

Controlled Assessment involves <u>answering two question papers</u> under exam conditions — but there's the added bonus of <u>doing an experiment</u> between them. Sounds thrilling.

There are Two Sections in the Controlled Assessment

(1) Planning

1) Before you do the Section 1 question paper you'll be given time to do some <u>research</u> into the topic that's been set. You should use lots of <u>different sources</u> (e.g. the internet, textbooks etc.).

2) You'll then need to develop a <u>hypothesis/prediction</u> and come up with <u>two</u> different methods to test it.

3) You'll also need to be able to <u>outline both methods</u> and say which one is <u>best</u> (and why it's the best one). Then describe the best method in <u>detail</u>.

4) You're allowed to write <u>notes</u> about your two methods on <u>one side of A4</u> and have them with you for both question papers. Make sure they cover:

- What variables you're going to <u>control</u> (and <u>how</u> you're going to control them).
- What <u>measurements</u> you're going to take.
- How you'd use a <u>trial run</u> to figure out the <u>range</u> and <u>interval</u> you'll use for the <u>independent variable</u>. See page 6 for more.
- What <u>range</u> and <u>interval</u> of values you will use for the <u>independent variable</u>.
- How many times you're going to <u>repeat</u> the experiment — at least <u>three</u> is a good idea.
- What <u>equipment</u> you're going to use (and <u>why</u> that equipment is <u>right for the job</u>).
- <u>How to carry out</u> the experiment, i.e. what you do first, what you do second...
- What <u>hazards</u> are involved in doing the experiment, and <u>how to reduce them</u>.
- What <u>table</u> you'll draw to put your results in. See p.8 for how to draw one that examiners will love.

There's lots of help on all of these things on pages 5-8.

When you've done the planning and completed the first question paper you'll actually <u>do the experiment</u>. Then you'll have to <u>present your data</u>.

After that it's onto the Section 2 question paper...

(2) Drawing Conclusions and Evaluating

For the Section 2 question paper you have to do these things for <u>your experiment</u>:

1) <u>Draw conclusions</u> from your results. For this you need to <u>describe the relationship</u> between the variables in <u>detail</u> — see the previous page for how to do this.

2) Say whether your results <u>back up the hypothesis/prediction</u>, and give reasons <u>why</u> or <u>why not</u>.

3) <u>Evaluate</u> your experiment. For this you need to <u>suggest ways you could improve your experiment</u>.

- Comment on your <u>equipment</u> and <u>method</u>, e.g. could you have used more <u>accurate</u> equipment?
- Make sure you <u>explain how</u> the improvements would give you <u>better data</u> next time.
- <u>Refer to your results</u>. E.g. 'I could use a more sensitive mass balance next time to work out a more accurate rate of reaction. This could have stopped me from getting the anomalous result in the second repeat of the experiment'.

You'll also be <u>given some secondary data</u> (data collected by other people) from experiments on the same topic and asked to <u>analyse it</u>.

This just involves doing what you did for your data with the secondary data, e.g. draw conclusions from it.

If that's controlled assessment, I'd hate to see uncontrolled assessment...

That might be an Everest-sized list of stuff, but it's <u>all important</u>. No need to panic at the sight of it though — as long as you've <u>learnt everything</u> on the previous few pages, you should be fine.

Cells

All living things are made of <u>cells</u>. If you don't believe me, look down a <u>microscope</u> and you'll see what I mean.

Plant and Animal Cells have Similarities and Differences

Most <u>human cells</u>, like most <u>animal</u> cells, have these parts:

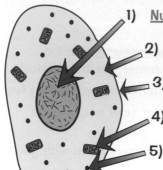

1) <u>Nucleus</u> — contains <u>DNA</u> that controls the activities of the cell.

2) <u>Cytoplasm</u> — gel-like substance where most of the <u>chemical reactions</u> happen.

3) <u>Cell membrane</u> — holds the cell together and controls what goes <u>in</u> and <u>out</u>.

4) <u>Mitochondria</u> — where most of the <u>energy</u> from <u>respiration</u> is released (see p. 26).

5) <u>Ribosomes</u> — these are where <u>proteins</u> are made in the cell.

Plant cells usually have <u>all the bits</u> that <u>animal</u> cells have, plus a few <u>extra</u> things that animal cells <u>don't</u> have:

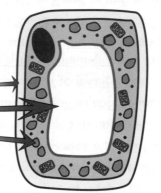

1) <u>Cell wall</u> — made of <u>cellulose</u>. It <u>strengthens</u> the cell.

2) <u>Permanent vacuole</u> — contains <u>cell sap</u>.

3) <u>Chloroplasts</u> — these <u>absorb</u> (take in) <u>light energy</u> to make <u>food</u> for the plant (see page 16).

> The cells of algae (e.g. seaweed) also have a cell wall and chloroplasts.

Yeast is a Single-Celled Organism

1) Yeast have only <u>one cell</u>.
2) A yeast cell has these bits:

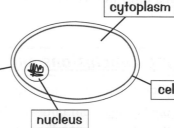

Bacterial Cells Have No Nucleus

1) Bacterial cells have these bits:
2) The <u>DNA</u> floats in the cytoplasm because they don't have a <u>nucleus</u>.

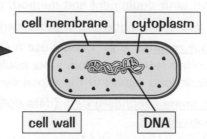

There's quite a bit to learn in biology — but that's life, I guess...

On this page are <u>typical cells</u> with all the typical bits you need to know. But cells <u>aren't</u> all the same — they <u>look</u> different and <u>make</u> different things depending on the <u>job</u> they do.

Diffusion

Particles <u>move about randomly</u> (they don't follow a pattern), and after a bit they end up <u>evenly spaced</u>.

Don't Be Put Off by the Fancy Word

1) "<u>Diffusion</u>" is just the <u>gradual</u> (slow) <u>movement</u> of particles from plaooo where there are <u>lots</u> of them to plaooo where there are <u>fewer</u> of them.

2) But you have to learn the fancy way of saying this:

> **<u>DIFFUSION</u> is the <u>spreading out</u> of <u>particles</u> from an area of <u>HIGH CONCENTRATION</u> to an area of <u>LOW CONCENTRATION</u>**

3) Diffusion happens in <u>solutions</u> and <u>gases</u>. For example, the smell of perfume diffuses through the air in a room:

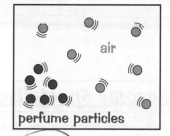

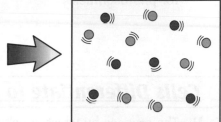

perfume particles

perfume particles diffused in the air

4) The <u>bigger</u> the <u>difference</u> in concentration, the <u>faster</u> the rate (speed) of diffusion.

Cell Membranes Are Kind of Clever...

1) They <u>hold</u> the cell together <u>BUT</u> they let stuff <u>in and out</u> as well.

2) Dissolved substances can move in and out of cells by <u>diffusion</u>.

3) Only very <u>small</u> molecules can <u>fit</u> through cell membranes, e.g. <u>oxygen</u>, <u>glucose</u> and <u>amino acids</u>.

4) <u>Big</u> molecules like <u>starch</u> and <u>proteins</u> can't fit through the membrane:

Oxygen is needed for respiration — see page 26.

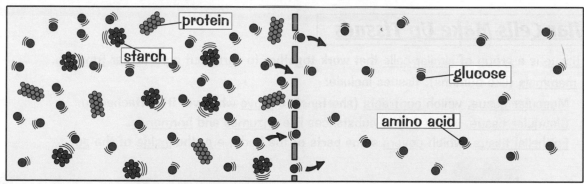

protein

starch

glucose

amino acid

5) Molecules move from where there's a <u>high concentration</u> (a lot of them) to where there's a <u>low concentration</u> (not such a lot of them).

6) They actually move <u>both</u> ways — but if there are a lot <u>more</u> molecules on one side of the membrane, there's a <u>net</u> (overall) movement <u>from</u> that side.

Revision by diffusion — you wish...

If only these words would diffuse into your mind, from an area of <u>high concentration</u> (in the book) to an area of <u>low concentration</u> (in your mind, no offence). It might happen if you read it again. Why don't you give it a go...

Specialised Cells and Tissues

Cells again. You need to know why _different types_ of plant cells (or animal cells) look different...

Specialised Cells have Special Features

Cells in a leaf

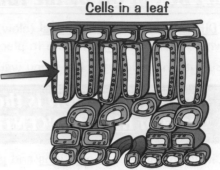

1) _Specialised cells_ are cells that carry out a specific _function_.

2) They have _special features_ that help them to carry out this function. For example, _palisade leaf cells_ carry out _lots of photosynthesis_. They contain _lots of chloroplasts_, which are needed for photosynthesis.

palisade leaf cell

There's more on photosynthesis on pages 16-18.

Cells Differentiate to Become Specialised

1) The _process_ by which a cell _changes_ to become specialised is called _differentiation_.

differentiation

unspecialised cell   specialised cell

2) Differentiation occurs as a _multicellular organism_ (like you, me or a plant) _develops_ (grows).

3) _Specialised cells_ form _tissues_, which form _organs_, which form _organ systems_ (see below and next page).

4) _Large multicellular organisms_ have different _systems_ inside them for _exchanging_ and _transporting_ materials.

Similar Cells Make Up Tissues

1) A _tissue_ is a _group_ of _similar cells_ that work together to carry out a particular _function_.

2) In _mammals_ (like humans), tissues include:

- _Muscular tissue_, which _contracts_ (shortens) to _move_ whatever it's attached to.
- _Glandular tissue_, which _makes_ substances like _enzymes_ and _hormones_.
- _Epithelial tissue_, which _covers_ some parts of the body, e.g. the _inside_ of the _gut_.

epithelial cell

epithelial tissue

Soft and quilted — the best kind of tissues...

Palisade cells and epithelial cells have all the typical bits shown on page 12. They just look completely different, that's all, because they do _totally different jobs_. Specialised, specialised, specialised — learn it, learn it, learn it.

Biology 2a — Cells, Organs and Populations

Organs and Organ Systems

Specialised cells form tissues (see last page). These tissues form organs. Organs form organ systems.

Tissues Make Up Organs

1) An organ is a group of different tissues that work together to perform a certain function.

2) The stomach is an organ made of these tissues:
   - Muscular tissue, which moves the stomach wall to churn (mix) up the food.
   - Glandular tissue, which makes digestive juices to digest food.
   - Epithelial tissue, which covers the outside and inside of the stomach.

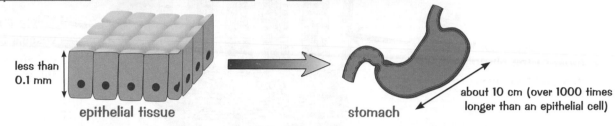

less than 0.1 mm

epithelial tissue

stomach

about 10 cm (over 1000 times longer than an epithelial cell)

Organs Make Up Organ Systems

1) An organ system is a group of organs working together to perform a particular function.

2) The digestive system is found in humans and other mammals.

3) The digestive system breaks down food. It does this by releasing digestive juices.

4) Then the digestive system absorbs (takes in) the products of digestion.

5) You need to know where all these organs are in the digestive system:

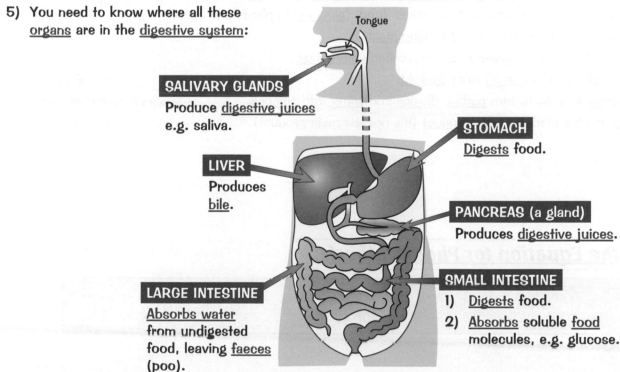

Tongue

SALIVARY GLANDS
Produce digestive juices e.g. saliva.

STOMACH
Digests food.

LIVER
Produces bile.

PANCREAS (a gland)
Produces digestive juices.

LARGE INTESTINE
Absorbs water from undigested food, leaving faeces (poo).

SMALL INTESTINE
1) Digests food.
2) Absorbs soluble food molecules, e.g. glucose.

You won't get much of a tune playing these organs...

Organ systems are made up of organs. Organs are made of tissues. Tissues are groups of cells working together.

Plant Structure and Photosynthesis

It's not just <u>humans</u> that are made up of <u>tissues</u> and <u>organs</u>, you know...

Plants Are Made Up of Tissues And Organs Too

1) <u>Plants</u> are made of <u>organs</u> like <u>stems</u>, <u>roots</u> and <u>leaves</u>.

2) <u>Leaves</u> are made of these <u>tissues</u>:

<u>Epidermal tissue</u> covers the whole plant.

<u>Mesophyll tissue</u> is where most of the <u>photosynthesis</u> in a plant occurs.

<u>Epidermal tissue</u>.

<u>Xylem</u> and <u>phloem</u> vessels transport substances around the plant.

Photosynthesis Makes Sugar Using Sunlight

1) <u>Photosynthesis</u> is the process that makes '<u>food</u>' (<u>glucose</u>) in plants and algae.

2) Photosynthesis happens inside the <u>chloroplasts</u>.

3) Chloroplasts contain a green substance called <u>chlorophyll</u>.

4) Chlorophyll absorbs <u>energy</u> from <u>sunlight</u>.

5) The energy is used to turn <u>carbon dioxide</u> and <u>water</u> into <u>glucose</u>.

6) <u>Oxygen</u> is also made as a <u>by-product</u> (it's not the main product).

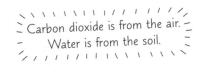
Carbon dioxide is from the air.
Water is from the soil.

Learn the Equation for Photosynthesis:

$$\text{Carbon dioxide} + \text{water} \xrightarrow[\text{chlorophyll}]{\text{SUNLIGHT}} \text{glucose} + \text{oxygen}$$

Now you've learnt something to bore your friends with...

You <u>must learn</u> the photosynthesis equation. Learn it so well that you'll <u>still</u> remember it even when you're <u>109</u>. It might look scary but it's not — it just tells you how <u>plants</u> make their <u>food</u>. So if you don't know it, <u>learn it</u>.

The Rate of Photosynthesis

Remember, photosynthesis is the process that makes glucose in plants and algae.

Light, Carbon Dioxide and Temperature are Limiting Factors

1) The rate of photosynthesis (how fast it happens) depends on:
   - how much light there is,
   - the amount of carbon dioxide (CO_2),
   - the temperature.

2) Any of these three factors can become the limiting factor.

3) A limiting factor is something that stops photosynthesis from going any faster.
   For example:
   - At night, light is the limiting factor.
   - In winter, it's often temperature that's the limiting factor.
   - If it's warm enough and bright enough then carbon dioxide will be the limiting factor.

Three Important Graphs for Rate of Photosynthesis

1) Not Enough Light Slows Down the Rate of Photosynthesis

1) At first, the more light there is, the faster photosynthesis happens.

2) This means the rate of photosynthesis depends on the amount of light. Light is the limiting factor.

3) After a certain point the graph flattens out. Here photosynthesis won't go any faster — even if you add more light.

4) This is because light is no longer the limiting factor. Now it's either the temperature or the amount of carbon dioxide that's the limiting factor.

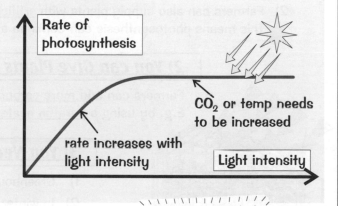

Rate of photosynthesis

CO_2 or temp needs to be increased

rate increases with light intensity

Light intensity

The amount of light is called light intensity.

2) Too Little Carbon Dioxide Also Slows it Down

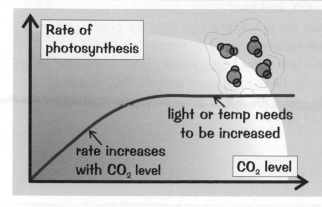

Rate of photosynthesis

light or temp needs to be increased

rate increases with CO_2 level

CO_2 level

1) The more carbon dioxide (CO_2) there is, the faster photosynthesis happens.

2) This means the amount of CO_2 is the limiting factor.

3) After a certain point, photosynthesis won't go any faster because CO_2 is no longer the limiting factor.

4) If there's plenty of light and carbon dioxide then it must be the temperature that's the limiting factor.

The Rate of Photosynthesis

3) The Temperature has to be Just Right

1) Usually, if the temperature is the <u>limiting factor</u> it's because it's <u>too low</u>.

2) This is because the <u>enzymes</u> (see page 23) needed for photosynthesis work more <u>slowly</u> at low temperatures.

3) But if the plant gets <u>too hot</u>, photosynthesis <u>won't happen at all</u>.

4) This is because the enzymes are <u>damaged</u> if the temperature's <u>too high</u> (over about 45 °C).

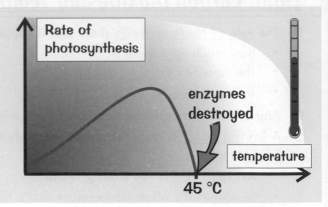

Rate of photosynthesis

enzymes destroyed

temperature

45 °C

You can Create Ideal Conditions for Farming in a Greenhouse

Farmers can make sure light, CO_2 and temperature <u>aren't limiting factors</u> by growing plants in a <u>greenhouse</u>.

1) You can Give Plants More Light

1) Greenhouses are made of <u>glass</u> so they let a lot of <u>light</u> through.

2) Farmers can also supply plants with <u>artificial light</u> (e.g. lots of lamps) at <u>night</u>. This means photosynthesis can continue at night.

2) You can Give Plants More Carbon Dioxide Too

Farmers can add <u>more carbon dioxide</u> inside the greenhouse. E.g. by using a <u>paraffin heater</u> that makes carbon dioxide as it burns.

3) You Need to Keep the Temperature Just Right

1) Greenhouses are <u>warm</u> because they <u>trap</u> the <u>sun's heat</u>.

2) In winter, farmers can use a <u>heater</u> to keep everything toasty warm.

3) In summer, they can use <u>shades</u> or <u>open windows</u> to cool things down.

1) Giving plants more light, CO_2 and heat <u>costs money</u>.
2) But if the farmer can keep the conditions <u>just right</u> for photosynthesis, the plants will grow much <u>faster</u>.
3) This means the farmer will get a <u>good crop</u> more <u>often</u>, which can be <u>sold</u>.
4) The farmer needs to supply the <u>right amount</u> of light, CO_2 and heat. It needs to be enough to make the plants grow well, but <u>not</u> more than the plants <u>need</u>, as this would just be <u>wasting money</u>.

Don't blame it on the sunshine, don't blame it on the CO_2...

...don't blame it on the temperature, blame it on the plant. Right, and now you'll never forget the <u>three limiting factors</u> in photosynthesis. No... well, make sure you read these pages over and over again till you do.

How Plants Use Glucose

Once plants have made <u>glucose</u> by <u>photosynthesis</u> (see p. 16), there are a few ways they can use it.

① __For Respiration__

1) Plants make <u>glucose</u> in their <u>leaves</u>.
2) They then use some of the glucose for <u>respiration</u> (see page 26).

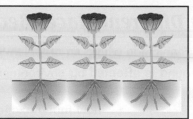

② __Making Cell Walls__

1) <u>Glucose</u> is made into <u>cellulose</u>.
2) Cellulose is used to make strong <u>cell walls</u> (see page 12).

③ __Making Proteins__

1) Plants absorb <u>nitrate ions</u> from the soil.
2) <u>Glucose</u> is joined with nitrate ions to make <u>amino acids</u>.
3) The amino acids are then made into <u>proteins</u>.

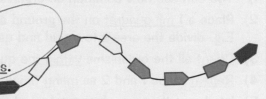

④ __Stored in Seeds__

<u>Glucose</u> is turned into <u>fats and oils</u> for storing in <u>seeds</u>. For example, we get <u>margarine</u> from <u>sunflower seeds</u>. Seeds also store <u>starch</u> (see below).

> Algae also use glucose to make cellulose for cell walls, fats and oils for storage, and amino acids for proteins.

⑤ __Stored as Starch__

1) <u>Glucose</u> is turned into <u>starch</u> and <u>stored</u> in roots, stems and leaves. For example, <u>potato</u> and <u>parsnip</u> plants store starch — we eat the swollen storage organs.
2) <u>Starch</u> is <u>insoluble</u> — it doesn't dissolve. This makes starch much <u>better</u> for <u>storing</u> than glucose.

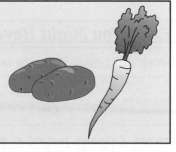

__Glucose is a very handy sugar__

So there are actually only <u>five things to learn</u> that plants do with glucose...
Right, shut the book and write down all the five uses of glucose. Bet you forget one. <u>Repeat until you don't</u>.

Distribution of Organisms

This is where the <u>fun</u> starts. Studying the <u>distribution</u> of organisms means you can get your hands <u>dirty</u> and look at some <u>real organisms</u>, living in the <u>wild</u>. Hold on to your hats folks...

Organisms Live in Different Places Because The Environment Varies

1) The <u>distribution</u> of an organism is <u>where</u> an organism is <u>found</u>.

2) Where an organism is found is affected by <u>environmental factors</u>, such as:

- the <u>temperature</u>
- how much <u>water</u> there is
- the amount of <u>light</u>
- how much <u>oxygen</u> and <u>carbon dioxide</u> there is
- if there are enough <u>nutrients</u> (food) around

3) An organism might be <u>more common</u> in <u>one area</u> than another due to <u>differences</u> in <u>environmental factors</u> between the two areas. For example, in a field, you might find that daisies are <u>more common</u> in the open, than under trees, because there's <u>more light</u>.

4) To <u>study</u> the distribution of an organism you can use <u>quadrats</u> or <u>transects</u> (see page 21).

Use Quadrats to Study The Distribution of Small Organisms

1) You can see how common an organism is in <u>two different areas</u> — these are called <u>sample areas</u>.

2) Place a <u>1 m² quadrat</u> on the ground at a <u>random point</u> within the <u>first</u> sample area. E.g. divide the area into a grid and use random number tables to pick coordinates.

3) <u>Count</u> all the organisms <u>within</u> the quadrat.

4) <u>Repeat</u> steps 1 and 2 as many times as you can.

5) <u>Work out</u> the <u>mean</u> (average) number of organisms per quadrat within the first sample area.

A quadrat

- For example, the numbers of daisies in 7 quadrats are: 7, 6, 7, 7, 5, 9, 8
- Here, the MEAN is: $\dfrac{\text{TOTAL number of organisms}}{\text{NUMBER of quadrats}} = \dfrac{49}{7} = \underline{7}$ daisies per quadrat.
- You also need to know about the MODE. It's the MOST COMMON value. In this example it's <u>7</u> too.
- And the MEDIAN is the MIDDLE value, when they're in order of size. It's <u>7</u> again.

6) <u>Repeat</u> steps 1 to 4 in the <u>second</u> sample area.

7) Finally <u>compare</u> the two means. E.g. you might find 1 daisy per m² in the shade, and 7 daisies per m² (lots more) in the open field.

In the Exam You Might Have to Work Out Population Size

You can work out <u>population size</u> using this equation...

$$\text{population size} = \dfrac{\text{mean number of organisms}}{\text{per 1 m}^2 \text{ quadrat}} \times \text{total area (in m}^2)$$

E.g. there are <u>7</u> daisies per m² in a <u>100 m²</u> field. So the population size = 7 x 100 = <u>700 daisies</u>.

Drat, drat, and double drat — my favourite use of quadrats...

You must put your quadrat down in a <u>random place</u> before you start counting. Even chucking the quadrat over your shoulder* is better than putting it down right on the <u>first big patch</u> of organisms that you see.

not an invitation to break equipment or hurt other students etc.

More on The Distribution of Organisms

So, now you think you've learnt <u>all about</u> distribution. Well <u>hold on</u> — there's <u>more fun</u> to be had.

Use Transects to Study The Distribution of Organisms Along a Line

You can use lines called <u>transects</u> to help find out how organisms (like plants) are <u>distributed</u> across an area. E.g. if an organism becomes <u>more or less common</u> as you move from a hedge towards the middle of a field. Here's what to do:

1) <u>Mark out a line</u> in the area you want to study using a tape measure.

2) <u>Collect data</u> along the line by:

- <u>Counting</u> all the organisms that <u>touch</u> the line.

- Using <u>quadrats</u> placed along the line.

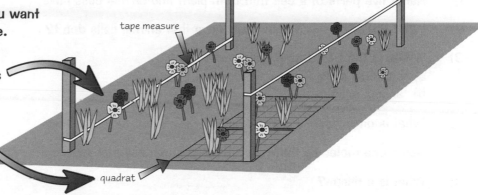

tape measure

quadrat

When Collecting Environmental Data You Need to Think About...

❶ Reliability

1) <u>Quadrats</u> and <u>transects</u> are <u>pretty good tools</u> for finding out how an organism is distributed.

2) But, you have to work hard to make sure your results are <u>reliable</u>. This means making sure your results are <u>repeatable</u> and <u>reproducible</u> (see page 3).

3) To make your results <u>more</u> reliable you need to:

- <u>Take a large sample size</u>
  E.g. use as <u>many</u> quadrats and transects as possible in your sample area.

- <u>Use random samples</u>
  E.g. <u>randomly</u> put down or mark out your quadrat or transect.

❷ Validity

1) For your results to be <u>valid</u> they must be <u>reliable</u> (see above) and <u>answer the original question</u>.

2) To answer the original question, you need to <u>control all the variables</u>.

3) The question you want to answer is whether a <u>difference in distribution</u> between two sample areas is <u>due</u> to a <u>difference in one environmental factor</u>.

4) If you've controlled all the <u>other variables</u> that could be affecting the distribution, you'll know whether a <u>difference in distribution</u> is caused by the <u>environmental factor</u> or not.

5) If you <u>don't</u> control the other variables, you won't know whether any correlation you've found is due to <u>chance</u>, the <u>environmental factor</u> you're looking at or because of a <u>different variable</u>. The study won't give you valid data.

A slug that's been run over — definitely a widely-spread organism...

In the exam, you may get the <u>results</u> of a study into the distribution of organisms and be asked questions on it. If you're asked about <u>reliability</u>, read the method carefully and think about the <u>sample size</u> and <u>random</u> samples.

Revision Summary for Biology 2a

And where do you think you're going? It's no use just reading through and thinking you've got it all — this stuff will only stick in your head if you've learnt it <u>properly</u>. And that's what these questions are for.
I won't pretend they're easy — they're not meant to be, but all the information is in the section somewhere.
Have a go at all the questions, then if there are any you can't answer, go back, look stuff up and try again.
Enjoy...

1)   Name five parts of a cell that both plant and animal cells have.

2)   What three things do plant cells have that animal cells don't?

3)   Where is the DNA found in:
     a) bacterial cells
     b) animal cells?

4)   What is diffusion?

5)   Name one molecule that can diffuse through cell membranes.

6)   What is a tissue?

7)   What is an organ?

8)   Give one example of a tissue in the human stomach, and say what job it does.

9)   Name one organ system found in the human body.

10) Give an example of a plant tissue and a plant organ.

11) What is the green substance in leaves that absorbs sunlight?

12) Write down the equation for photosynthesis.

13) Name the three factors that can limit the rate of photosynthesis.

14) Explain why it's important that a plant doesn't get too hot.

15) Describe one thing that a farmer could do to make sure she grows a good crop of tomatoes in her greenhouse.

16) Give two ways that plants can use the glucose produced by photosynthesis.

17) Give three environmental factors that can affect the distribution of organisms.

18) Briefly describe how you could find out how common an organism is in two sample areas using quadrats.

19) Describe one way of using a transect to find out how an organism is distributed across an area.

Enzymes

Chemical reactions are what make you work. And enzymes are what make them work.

Enzymes Are Catalysts

1) Living things have tons of chemical reactions going on inside them all the time.
2) They produce enzymes that speed up the chemical reactions.
3) Enzymes are biological catalysts.

> A **CATALYST** is a substance which **INCREASES** the speed of a reaction, without being **CHANGED** or **USED UP** in the reaction.

4) All enzymes are proteins.
5) Proteins are made up of chains of amino acids.
6) These chains are folded into a specific shape. This specific shape allows the enzyme to do its job.
7) As well as catalysts, proteins act as:

   • structural parts of tissues (e.g. muscles)
   • hormones
   • antibodies

Enzymes Have Special Shapes

1) Chemical reactions usually involve things either being split apart or joined together.
2) Every enzyme has a specific shape that fits onto the substance involved in a reaction.
3) Enzymes are really picky — they usually only catalyse one reaction.
4) This is because, for the enzyme to work, the substance has to fit its special shape.
   If the substance doesn't match the enzyme's shape, then the reaction won't be catalysed.

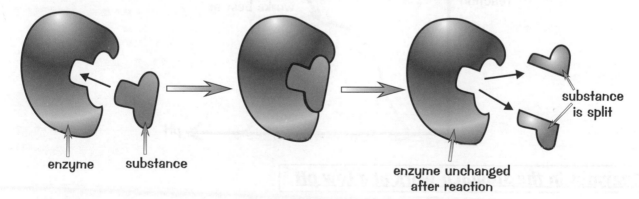

enzyme   substance

enzyme unchanged after reaction

substance is split

If only enzymes could speed up revision...

Just like you've got to have the correct key for a lock, you've got to have the right substance for an enzyme. If the substance doesn't fit, the enzyme won't catalyse the reaction...

More on Enzymes

Changing the <u>temperature</u> changes the <u>rate</u> (speed) of a reaction involving an <u>enzyme</u>...

Enzymes *Need the Right Temperature*

1) At first, a <u>higher</u> temperature <u>increases</u> the rate of a reaction involving an enzyme.
2) But if it gets <u>too hot</u>, some of the <u>bonds</u> holding the enzyme together <u>break</u>.
3) This destroys the enzyme's <u>special shape</u> and so it won't work any more — the enzyme is <u>denatured</u>.

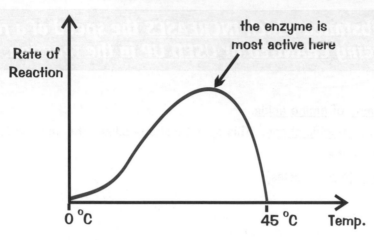

Enzymes *Need the Right pH Too*

1) <u>Changing</u> the <u>pH</u> can also change the <u>rate</u> of a <u>reaction</u> involving an enzyme.
2) If the pH is <u>too high</u> or <u>too low</u>, it affects the <u>bonds</u> holding the enzyme together.
3) This changes the shape and <u>denatures</u> the enzyme.
4) All enzymes have a <u>pH</u> that they <u>work best at</u>.

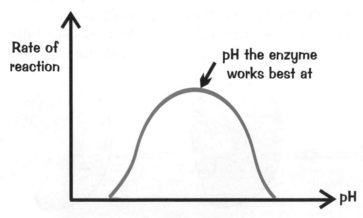

Enzymes in the Stomach Work at a Low pH

1) The <u>stomach</u> produces an acid called <u>hydrochloric acid</u>.
2) Enzymes in the stomach work best in these <u>acidic conditions</u>.

Some like it hot — but not enzymes...

Enzymes are a bit like <u>Goldilocks</u> — they like things not too cold, not too hot, but <u>just right</u>. Fussy little things. The stomach enzymes are worse, they like bathing in <u>acid</u> — that's just odd. Think of them when revising this...

Enzymes and Digestion

Some enzymes work <u>outside</u> cells. For example, enzymes in digestion are made by <u>specialised cells</u> in the <u>glands</u> and <u>gut lining</u>. Then they're <u>released</u> into the <u>gut</u> to <u>mix</u> with <u>food</u>. Makes sense, really.

Digestive Enzymes Break Down Big Molecules into Smaller Ones

1) <u>Starch</u>, <u>proteins</u> and <u>fats</u> are BIG molecules.
   They're too big to pass through the walls of the digestive system.

2) <u>Sugars</u>, <u>amino acids</u>, <u>glycerol</u> and <u>fatty acids</u> are much smaller molecules.
   They can pass easily through the walls of the digestive system.

3) The BIG molecules are broken down into the smaller ones by <u>digestive enzymes</u>.

AMYLASE
1) Amylase is made in the <u>salivary glands</u>, <u>pancreas</u>, and <u>small intestine</u>.
2) It works in the <u>mouth</u> and <u>small intestine</u>.

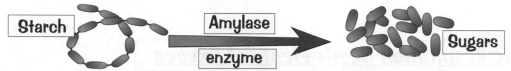

PROTEASE
1) Protease is made in the <u>stomach</u>, <u>pancreas</u> and <u>small intestine</u>.
2) It works in the <u>stomach</u> and <u>small intestine</u>.

LIPASE
1) Lipase is made in the <u>pancreas</u> and <u>small intestine</u>.
2) It works in the <u>small intestine</u>.

The structure of the digestive system is shown on page 15.

Lipids are fats and oils.

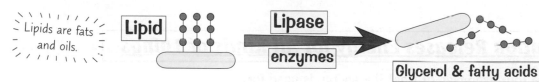

Bile Neutralises the Stomach Acid

1) Bile is <u>produced</u> in the <u>liver</u>.
2) It's <u>stored</u> in the <u>gall bladder</u> before it's released into the <u>small intestine</u>.
3) Bile is <u>alkaline</u>. It <u>neutralises</u> the acid added to food in the stomach and makes conditions <u>alkaline</u>.
4) The enzymes in the small intestine <u>work best</u> in these alkaline conditions.

What do you call an acid that's eaten all the pies...

This all happens inside your <u>digestive system</u> — it gets a load of <u>food</u>, <u>digestive juices</u> and <u>enzymes</u> piled into it.
Most of it's then absorbed back into the body and the rest is politely stored ready for removal.

Enzymes and Respiration

Many chemical reactions inside cells are controlled by enzymes — including the ones in respiration.

Respiration is NOT "Breathing In and Out"

1) All living things respire.
2) Respiration is the process of releasing energy from the breakdown of glucose (a sugar).
3) Respiration releases the energy that the cell needs to do just about everything.

> **RESPIRATION is the process of RELEASING ENERGY FROM GLUCOSE, which goes on IN EVERY CELL**

Aerobic Respiration Needs Plenty of Oxygen

1) Aerobic respiration is respiration using oxygen.
2) Aerobic respiration goes on all the time in plants and animals.
3) Most of the reactions in aerobic respiration happen inside mitochondria (see page 12).
4) You need to learn the overall word equation:

> **Glucose + oxygen $\implies$ carbon dioxide + water + ENERGY**

Aerobic Respiration Releases Energy for All Kinds of Things

You need to learn these four examples of what the energy is used for:

1) To build up larger molecules from smaller ones.

2) In animals, to allow the muscles to contract.

3) In mammals and birds the energy is used to keep their body temperature steady.

4) In plants, to build sugars, nitrates and other nutrients into amino acids. Amino acids are then built up into proteins.

Lots of molecules found aerobics tough, but only glucose broke down...

So... respiration — that's a pretty important thing. It's pretty important that you know what it's all about too. Keep re-reading this page until you can say what aerobic respiration is whilst standing on your head and clapping.

Exercise

When you exercise, your body adapts so that your muscles get <u>more oxygen and glucose</u>.

Exercise Increases the Heart Rate

1) Your muscle cells use <u>oxygen</u> to <u>release energy</u> from <u>glucose</u> — they respire aerobically.

2) The energy is used to <u>contract</u> the muscles.

3) When you <u>exercise</u>...
   - Your muscle cells need <u>more oxygen</u> and <u>glucose</u> (for respiration).
   - Extra <u>carbon dioxide</u> needs to be <u>removed</u> from the muscle cells.
   - For these things to happen, the <u>blood</u> has to flow at a <u>faster rate</u>.

4) This is why exercise:
   - <u>increases</u> your <u>breathing rate</u>,
   - makes you breathe <u>more deeply</u>,
   - <u>increases</u> your <u>heart rate</u>.

Glycogen is Used During Exercise

1) Your muscles store <u>glucose</u> as <u>glycogen</u>.

2) During hard exercise, muscles use glucose <u>quickly</u>.

3) So some of the stored glycogen is changed back to <u>glucose</u> to give <u>more energy</u>.

Anaerobic Respiration is Used if There's Not Enough Oxygen

1) When you do hard exercise, your body can't supply enough <u>oxygen</u> to your muscles. This means they start doing <u>anaerobic respiration</u>.

2) <u>Anaerobic respiration</u> is respiration <u>without</u> oxygen.

3) It's the <u>incomplete</u> breakdown of glucose (the glucose isn't broken down properly).

4) Anaerobic respiration is <u>**NOT the best way to convert glucose into energy**</u>.

5) This is because it makes <u>lactic acid</u>. The lactic acid builds up in the muscles and gets <u>painful</u>.

6) Lactic acid also causes <u>muscle fatigue</u> — the muscles get <u>tired</u> and <u>stop contracting as well</u>.

7) <u>Blood</u> flowing through your muscles <u>removes</u> the lactic acid.

I've got tons of energy — I don't need anaerobic respir...zzzzzzzzzz

Phew... bet you're well tired after reading all this. Still, it needs learning before you have a rest. In the exam, you could be asked about the <u>effects of exercise</u> on the body — so make sure you really do <u>know this page</u>.

Uses of Enzymes

Some <u>microorganisms</u> make enzymes which pass <u>out</u> of their cells. The enzymes then catalyse reactions outside the cells, like digesting the microorganisms' food. These enzymes have many <u>uses</u>...

Enzymes Are Used in Biological Detergents

1) <u>Enzymes</u> are the '<u>biological</u>' ingredients in <u>biological detergents</u> (washing powders).

2) They're mainly <u>protein-digesting</u> enzymes (<u>proteases</u>) and <u>fat-digesting</u> enzymes (<u>lipases</u>).

3) Biological detergents are <u>more effective</u> at working at <u>low temperatures</u> than other types of detergents.

Enzymes Are Used to Change Foods

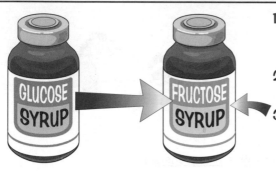

1) The <u>proteins</u> in some <u>baby foods</u> are '<u>pre-digested</u>' (they've already been broken down) using protein-digesting enzymes (<u>proteases</u>). This means they're easier for the baby to digest.

2) Carbohydrate-digesting enzymes (<u>carbohydrases</u>) can be used to turn <u>starch syrup</u> (yuk) into <u>sugar syrup</u> (yum).

3) <u>Glucose syrup</u> can be turned into <u>fructose syrup</u> using an <u>isomerase</u> enzyme. Fructose is <u>sweeter</u>, so you can use <u>less</u> of it — good for slimming foods and drinks.

Using Enzymes in Industry Saves Money

Enzymes are <u>really useful</u> in industry — they <u>speed up</u> reactions without the need for <u>high temperatures</u> and <u>pressures</u>. You need to learn these points about using enzymes in industry.

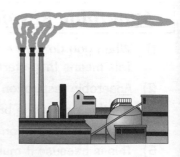

ADVANTAGE

Using lower temperatures and pressures means a <u>lower cost</u> as it <u>saves energy</u>.

DISADVANTAGES

1) Enzymes can be <u>denatured</u> (they don't work any more) by even a <u>small</u> rise in temperature.

2) Enzymes can be <u>expensive</u> to produce.

There's a lot to learn — but don't be deterred gents...

Enzymes are great if you're a bit of a messy eater like me. When I put my shirt into the wash the <u>enzymes</u> in <u>washing powder</u> break down the big food molecules into smaller ones, which are washed away in water. <u>Genius</u>.

DNA

The first step in understanding genetics is getting to grips with DNA.

Chromosomes Are Really Long Molecules of DNA

1) <u>DNA</u> stands for <u>d</u>eoxyribonucleic <u>a</u>cid.
2) It contains all the <u>instructions</u> to put an organism together and <u>make it work</u>.
3) DNA is found in the <u>nucleus</u> of animal and plant cells.
4) It's found in really <u>long molecules</u> called <u>chromosomes</u>.
5) DNA has a <u>double helix structure</u> (two spirals that are twisted round each other, a bit like a <u>twisted ladder</u>).
6) A <u>gene</u> is a <u>section</u> of DNA.

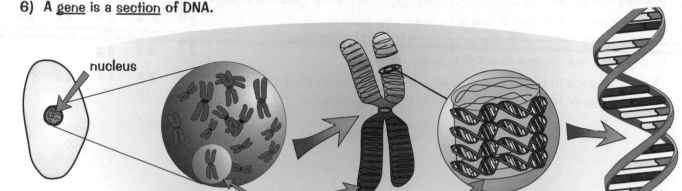

nucleus

single chromosome

gene

A DNA molecule with a double helix structure.

Everyone has Unique DNA

1) Everyone's DNA is <u>unique</u> (one of a kind)... apart from <u>identical twins</u>, who have the same DNA.
2) <u>DNA fingerprinting</u> is a way of <u>cutting up</u> a person's DNA into small sections and then <u>separating</u> them.
3) Every person's DNA fingerprint has a <u>unique</u> pattern (unless they're identical twins).
4) This means you can <u>tell people apart</u> by <u>comparing samples</u> of their DNA.
5) DNA fingerprinting is used in <u>forensic science</u>. E.g. DNA taken from a <u>crime scene</u> can be <u>compared</u> with DNA samples taken from <u>suspects</u>.

Suspect 1's DNA matches the DNA from a crime scene. So suspect 1 was probably at the crime scene.

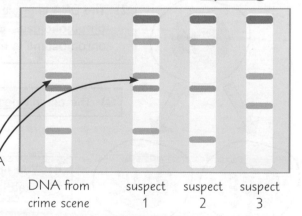

DNA from crime scene   suspect 1   suspect 2   suspect 3

So the trick is — frame your twin and they'll never get you...

If you're going to get anywhere with genetics, you need to make sure you know what <u>DNA</u> is, what <u>chromosomes</u> are, and what a <u>gene</u> is. Get this sorted and you'll find everything else a breeze.*

*Hopefully. Fingers crossed. Touch wood.

Mitosis

In order to <u>survive</u> and <u>grow</u>, our cells have got to be able to <u>divide</u>. And that means our <u>DNA</u> as well...

Mitosis Makes New Cells for Growth and Repair

1) <u>Body cells</u> normally have <u>two copies</u> of each <u>chromosome</u>.

2) They get one copy of each chromosome from the '<u>mother</u>', and one from the '<u>father</u>'.

3) So, humans have two copies of chromosome 1, two copies of chromosome 2, etc.

4) The diagram shows the <u>23 pairs of chromosomes</u> from a human cell. ▶

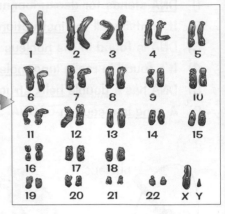

5) When a body cell <u>divides</u> it needs to make new cells <u>identical</u> to the <u>original</u> cell — with the <u>same number</u> of chromosomes.

6) This type of cell division is called <u>mitosis</u>.

7) Mitosis happens in plants and animals. It happens when they want to <u>grow</u> or to <u>replace</u> cells that have been <u>damaged</u>.

"<u>MITOSIS</u> is when a cell copies itself <u>by splitting</u> to form <u>two identical offspring</u>."

1) A cell with <u>two sets of chromosomes</u>.

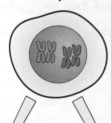

2) The DNA is <u>copied</u> and forms <u>X-shaped</u> <u>chromosomes</u>. Each 'arm' of the chromosome is an <u>exact copy</u> of the other. ▶

The left arm has the same DNA as the right arm of the chromosome.

3) The cell <u>divides once</u>.

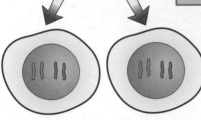

4) You now have <u>two new cells</u> containing exactly the same DNA — they're <u>identical</u>.

A cell's favourite computer game — divide and conquer...

This can seem tricky at first. But <u>don't worry</u> — just go through it <u>slowly</u>, one step at a time.
This type of division produces <u>identical cells</u>, but there's another type which doesn't... (see next page)

Asexual and Sexual Reproduction

Hang on, where are you off to — we're just getting on to the good stuff...

Asexual Reproduction Uses Mitosis

1) Some organisms reproduce by mitosis. For example, strawberry plants can reproduce this way.
2) This is an example of asexual reproduction.
3) The offspring have exactly the same genes as the parent — so there's no variation.
4) Other organisms (like humans) reproduce sexually. Oooo errr, read on...

Meiosis Makes New Sex Cells

1) Gametes are sex cells, e.g. sperm cells, egg cells.
2) Cells in your reproductive organs (testes or ovaries) divide to form gametes.
3) This type of cell division is called meiosis.
4) Gametes only have one set of chromosomes.

Sexual Reproduction Involves Gametes

1) During sexual reproduction, gametes combine to form a new individual.
2) First is fertilisation — the sperm and the egg join to form a new body cell.

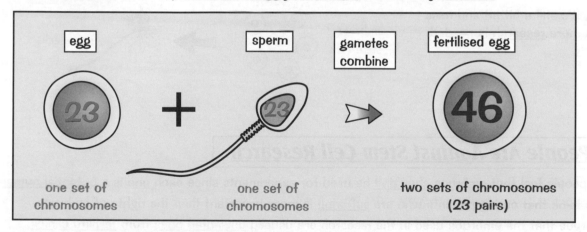

3) Then this new cell grows by dividing by mitosis.
4) The new individual will have a mixture of two sets of chromosomes (from the sperm and the egg). This means it will inherit features from both parents. This is how sexual reproduction produces variation.

Now that I have your undivided attention...

Remember, in humans, meiosis only occurs in reproductive organs where gametes are being made.

Stem Cells

Stem cell research is quite <u>exciting</u>... but not everyone agrees it should be done.

Embryonic Stem Cells Can Turn into ANY Type of Cell

1) <u>Differentiation</u> is the process by which a cell <u>changes</u> to become <u>specialised</u> for its job (see page 14).

2) In most <u>animal</u> cells, the ability to differentiate is <u>lost</u> at an early stage. But lots of <u>plant</u> cells <u>don't</u> ever lose this ability.

3) Some cells are <u>undifferentiated</u>. They can develop into <u>different types</u> of cells. These cells are called <u>STEM CELLS</u>.

4) There are <u>two main types</u> of stem cell:

1) Embryonic Stem Cells

- These are <u>unspecialised</u> cells found in early <u>embryos</u>.
- They have the potential to turn into <u>ANY</u> kind of cell.

2) Adult Stem Cells

- These are <u>unspecialised</u> cells found in adult animals.
- They can turn into <u>many</u> cell types (but <u>not all</u> cell types).

An embryo is an unborn baby at a very early stage of growth.

Our scientists believe they have found a potentially limitless supply of stem cells...

Stem Cells May Be Able to Cure Many Diseases

1) Scientists can <u>extract</u> stem cells from very early human embryos and <u>grow</u> them.

2) These stem cells could be used to <u>replace faulty cells</u> in sick people. E.g. you could make <u>nerve cells</u> for people <u>paralysed by injuries to the spine</u>.

3) So far, it's still a bit hit and miss — lots more <u>research</u> is needed.

embryonic stem cells 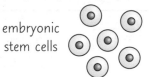  nerve cells

Some People Are Against Stem Cell Research

1) Some people feel that embryos <u>shouldn't</u> be used for experiments since each one is a <u>potential human life</u>.

2) Others think that curing patients who are <u>suffering</u> is more important than the rights of <u>embryos</u>.

3) They argue that the embryos used in the research are usually <u>unwanted ones</u> from <u>fertility clinics</u>. If they weren't used for research, they would probably just be <u>destroyed</u>.

4) But some people think scientists should be finding <u>other sources</u> of stem cells to use, so that people can be helped <u>without</u> having to use embryos.

Embryonic stem cells — the original Jack of all trades...

The <u>potential</u> of stem cells is <u>huge</u> — but it's <u>early days</u> yet and there are a lot of <u>issues</u> to think about.

X and Y Chromosomes

Chromosomes are really long molecules of DNA. Now for two very important little chromosomes...

Your Chromosomes Control Whether You're Male or Female

1) There are <u>23 pairs</u> of <u>chromosomes</u> in every human body cell.

2) The <u>23rd pair</u> are labelled <u>XX</u> or <u>XY</u>.

3) They're the two chromosomes that decide whether you turn out <u>male</u> or <u>female</u>.

All men have an <u>X</u> and a <u>Y</u> chromosome: **XY**   The <u>Y</u> chromosome causes <u>male characteristics</u>.

All women have <u>two X chromosomes</u>: **XX**   Having <u>two Xs</u> allows <u>female characteristics</u> to develop.

4) <u>Sperm cells</u> have an <u>X or a Y</u> chromosome.

5) All <u>eggs cells</u> have <u>one X</u> chromosome.

Genetic Diagrams Show the Probability of Having a Boy or a Girl

1) To find the <u>probability</u> of getting a boy or a girl, you can draw a <u>genetic diagram</u>.

2) Put the <u>possible gametes</u> from <u>one</u> parent down the side, and those from the <u>other</u> parent along the top.

3) Then in each square you <u>fill in</u> the letters from the top and side that line up with that square.

4) The <u>pairs of letters</u> in the square show the possible offspring you can end up with.

5) There are <u>two XX results</u> and <u>two XY results</u>, so there's the same probability of getting a boy or a girl.

6) Don't forget that this <u>50:50 ratio</u> is only a <u>probability</u> at each pregnancy. If you had four kids they <u>could</u> all be <u>boys</u> — yes I know, terrifying isn't it?

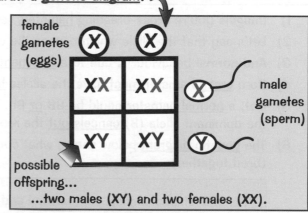

possible offspring... ...two males (XY) and two females (XX).

The other type of genetic diagram looks a bit harder, but it shows exactly the same thing.

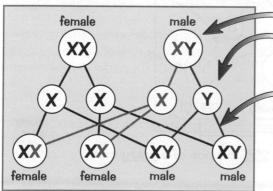

1) At the top are the <u>parents</u>.

2) The middle circles show the <u>possible gametes</u> that are formed. One gamete from the female combines with one gamete from the male (during fertilisation).

3) The criss-cross lines show <u>all</u> the <u>possible</u> ways the X and Y chromosomes <u>could</u> combine. The <u>possible offspring</u> you could get are shown in the bottom circles.

4) Remember, only <u>one</u> of these possibilities would <u>actually happen</u> for any one offspring.

Have you got the Y-factor...

The genetic diagrams here show a <u>chromosome</u> but most of the ones you'll see in the exams will show a <u>gene</u>. Don't worry — the principle's the same and there are loads of examples on the following pages.

Genetic Diagrams

Genetic diagrams are really handy for working out how characteristics are passed on. The diagrams aren't too scary — honest. I've given you an example using a crazy hamster, so it can't be that bad.

Genetic Diagrams Show the Possible Genes of Offspring

1) Different genes control the development of different characteristics, e.g. eye colour.
2) There can be different versions of the same gene. These are called alleles.
3) These alleles give different versions of a characteristic, e.g. blue eyes or brown eyes.
4) You have two alleles for each gene.
5) Alleles can be dominant or recessive.
6) If you have two dominant alleles, the dominant characteristic will be shown.
7) If you have one dominant and one recessive allele, only the dominant characteristic will be shown.
8) To show a recessive characteristic, both alleles for a gene have to be recessive.

You Need to Use and Understand Genetic Diagrams

1) Imagine you're cross-breeding hamsters, and that some behave normally while others do crazy acrobatics.
2) Let's say that the allele which causes the crazy behaviour is recessive — so use a 'b'.
3) And normal behaviour is due to a dominant allele — call it 'B'.
4) So a crazy hamster must have the alleles bb.
5) But, a normal hamster could be BB or Bb, because the dominant allele (B) cancels out the recessive one (b).

In genetic diagrams, capital letters represent dominant alleles and small letters represent recessive alleles.

6) The genetic diagram below shows what could happen when two normal hamsters (Bb) are crossed (bred together):

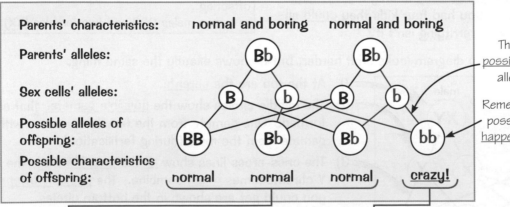

The lines show all the possible ways the parents' alleles could combine.

Remember, only one of these possibilities would actually happen for any one offspring.

There's a 75% chance of having a normal hamster, and a 25% chance of a crazy one.

7) This gives a 3:1 ratio of normal:crazy offspring.

It's not just hamsters that have the crazy allele...

... my sister has it too. Remember, 'results' like this are only probabilities. It doesn't mean it will actually happen.

The Work of Mendel

You can't learn about <u>genetics</u> without knowing about <u>Gregor Mendel</u>. He was a <u>monk</u> way back in the <u>1800s</u>.

Mendel Did Genetic Experiments with Pea Plants

1) <u>Gregor Mendel</u> studied how <u>characteristics</u> in <u>plants</u> were <u>passed on</u> from parents to their offspring.
2) The diagrams show two <u>crosses for height</u> in <u>pea plants</u> that Mendel carried out...

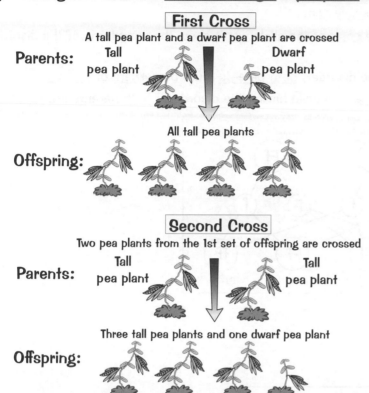

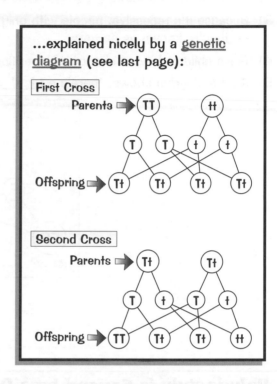

...explained nicely by a <u>genetic diagram</u> (see last page):

Mendel's experiments had shown that the height characteristic in pea plants was determined by separately inherited units passed on from each parent. The ratios of tall and dwarf plants in the offspring showed that the unit for tall plants, <u>T</u>, was <u>dominant</u> over the unit for dwarf plants, <u>t</u>.

Mendel Reached Three Important Conclusions

Mendel reached these three important conclusions about <u>inheritance in plants</u>:

1) Characteristics in plants are determined by inherited <u>units</u>.
2) Units are passed on from both parents, <u>one unit</u> from <u>each parent</u>.
3) Units can be <u>dominant</u> or <u>recessive</u> — if an individual has <u>both</u> the dominant and the recessive unit for a characteristic, the <u>dominant</u> characteristic will be expressed.

We now know that these "units" are <u>genes</u>. But in Mendel's time <u>nobody</u> knew anything about genes or DNA, and so the <u>importance</u> of his work was not realised until <u>after his death</u>.

Clearly, being a monk in the 1800s was a right laugh...

There was no TV back then, so monks had to make their <u>own entertainment</u>. And for Mendel this meant growing lots of <u>peas</u>. He was a clever guy... but a bit <u>ahead of his time</u>. Nobody had a clue what he was going on about.

Genetic Disorders

The alleles of some genes can be <u>faulty</u> which can cause some pretty <u>nasty</u> disorders. Because these disorders are a genetic problem, they can be <u>passed on</u> from parents to children.

Cystic Fibrosis is Caused by a Recessive Allele

1) <u>Cystic fibrosis</u> is a <u>genetic disorder</u> of the <u>cell membranes</u>.

2) It's caused by a faulty <u>recessive</u> allele of a <u>single gene</u>, 'f'.

3) Because it's recessive, people with only <u>one copy</u> of the allele <u>won't</u> show the symptoms of the disorder — they're known as <u>carriers</u>.

4) For a child to have a chance of inheriting the disorder, <u>both parents</u> must be <u>carriers</u> or <u>sufferers</u>.

5) As the diagram shows, there's a <u>1 in 4 chance</u> of a child having the disorder if <u>both</u> parents are <u>carriers</u>.

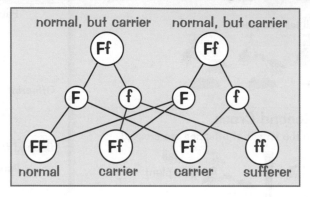

Polydactyly is Caused by a Dominant Allele

1) <u>Polydactyly</u> is a <u>genetic disorder</u> where a baby's born with <u>extra fingers or toes</u>.

2) It's cause by a faulty <u>dominant</u> allele of a <u>single gene</u>, '<u>D</u>'.

3) So polydactyly can be inherited if just <u>one parent</u> carries the faulty allele.

4) The <u>parent</u> that <u>has</u> the faulty allele will be a <u>sufferer</u> too, since the allele is <u>dominant</u>.

5) As the diagram shows, there's a <u>50% chance</u> of a child having the disorder if <u>one</u> parent has the D allele.

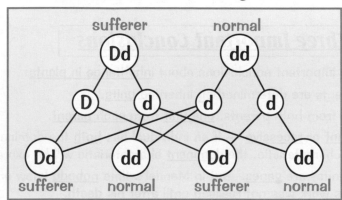

Unintentional mooning — caused by faulty genes...

You only need to know these <u>two genetic disorders</u>, so make sure you know this page fully <u>before</u> you move on.

Family Trees and Embryo Screening

Just when you thought you'd finished with genetic diagrams, these things called family trees show up...

You Need to be Able to Interpret Family Trees

1) The diagram on the right is a family tree for cystic fibrosis.

2) From the diagram you can tell that the allele for cystic fibrosis isn't dominant. This is because plenty of the family carry the allele but aren't sufferers.

3) There is a 25% chance that the new baby will be a sufferer. And there's a 50% chance that it will be a carrier. This is because both of the baby's parents are carriers (Eve and Phil are both Ff).

4) The case of the new baby is just the same as in the genetic diagram at the top of page 36. The baby could be normal (FF), a carrier (Ff) or a sufferer (ff).

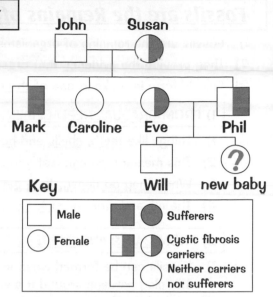

Key

☐ Male		■ ⬤	Sufferers
◯ Female		◨ ◖	Cystic fibrosis carriers
		☐ ◯	Neither carriers nor sufferers

Embryos Can Be Screened for Genetic Disorders

1) During *in vitro* fertilisation (IVF), embryos are fertilised in a lab and then put into the mother's womb.

2) Before they're put into the mother, you can remove a cell from each embryo and look at its genes. This is called embryo screening.

3) Many genetic disorders can be picked up in this way, such as cystic fibrosis.

4) Embryos with 'good' alleles are then put into the mother — the ones with 'bad' alleles are destroyed.

5) There are lots of arguments for and against embryo screening...

Against Embryo Screening

1) There may come a point where everyone wants to screen their embryos so they can pick the 'best' one, e.g. they want a blond-haired, clever boy.

2) The embryos with 'bad' alleles are destroyed — they could have developed into humans.

3) Screening is expensive.

For Embryo Screening

1) It will help to stop people suffering.

2) There are laws to stop it going too far. At the moment parents can't even choose the sex of their baby (unless it's for health reasons).

3) Treating disorders costs money.

Many people think that embryo screening isn't right for genetic disorders that don't affect a person's health, such as polydactyly.

Embryo screening — it's a tricky one...

In the exam, you might get a family tree showing a dominant allele. If so then there won't be any carriers shown. Or, you could be asked to describe the issues for and against embryo screening, so learn the ones listed above.

Fossils

If a fossil has been <u>preserved</u> (well-kept), you can see what really old creatures used to <u>look</u> like. Cool.

Fossils are the Remains of Plants and Animals

1) Fossils are the <u>remains</u> of organisms from <u>many years ago</u>, which are found in <u>rocks</u>.

2) They provide the <u>evidence</u> that organisms lived ages ago.

3) Fossils form in rocks in one of <u>three</u> ways:

1) FROM <u>GRADUAL REPLACEMENT</u> BY MINERALS (Most fossils happen this way.)

1) Things like <u>teeth</u>, <u>shells</u> and <u>bones</u> don't easily decay.

2) This means they can last a <u>long time</u> when <u>buried</u>.

3) When they do decay, they get <u>replaced by minerals</u>.

4) The minerals form a <u>rock-like substance</u> shaped like the original hard part.

2) FROM <u>CASTS</u> AND <u>IMPRESSIONS</u>

1) Fossils can be formed when an organism is <u>buried</u> in a <u>soft</u> material like <u>clay</u>. The clay <u>hardens</u> around it and the organism <u>decays</u>. The organism leaves a <u>cast</u> of itself. An animal's <u>burrow</u> or a plant's <u>roots</u> can also be preserved as casts.

2) Things like <u>footprints</u> are <u>pressed</u> into soft materials. This leaves an <u>impression</u> when they harden.

3) FROM <u>PRESERVATION</u> IN PLACES WHERE NO DECAY HAPPENS

1) <u>Decay microbes</u> only work if there's <u>oxygen</u>, <u>moisture</u>, <u>warmth</u> and the right <u>pH</u>.

2) In <u>some substances</u> these conditions <u>aren't</u> all <u>present</u> so decay doesn't happen. For example, there's <u>no oxygen</u> or <u>moisture</u> in <u>amber</u> so decay organisms can't survive.

A preserved organism in amber.

But No One Knows How Life Began

1) Fossils show how many of today's species have <u>evolved</u> (changed and developed) over <u>millions of years</u>.

2) There are lots of <u>hypotheses</u> suggesting how life first came into being. For example:

- Maybe the <u>first life forms</u> appeared in a <u>swamp</u> (or under the <u>sea</u>) here on <u>Earth</u>.

- Or maybe simple carbon molecules were brought here on <u>comets</u> and developed into simple life forms. But no one really knows.

3) These hypotheses can't be supported or disproved because there's a <u>lack</u> of <u>valid</u> and <u>reliable</u> evidence.

4) There's a lack of evidence because many early organisms were <u>soft-bodied</u>. Soft tissue tends to decay away <u>completely</u>. So the fossil record is <u>incomplete</u> (unfinished).

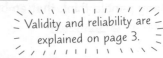
Validity and reliability are explained on page 3.

5) Plus, fossils that did form millions of years ago may have been <u>destroyed</u> by <u>geological activity</u>. E.g. the movement of tectonic plates may have <u>crushed</u> fossils already formed in the rock.

Don't get swamped by all this information...

Right, testing time... scribble down the <u>three ways</u> that fossils form and why we can't be sure <u>how life began</u>.

Extinction and Speciation

Evolution leads to the development of lots of <u>different species</u>. But not every species is still around today... :(

Extinction Happens if You Can't Evolve Quickly Enough

1) The fossil record contains many species that <u>don't exist any more</u> — these species are said to be <u>extinct</u>.

2) Species become extinct for these reasons:

- The <u>environment changes</u> too quickly (e.g. their habitat is destroyed).
- A <u>new predator</u> kills them all (e.g. humans hunting them).
- A <u>new disease</u> kills them all.
- They can't <u>compete</u> with another (new) species for <u>food</u>.
- A <u>catastrophic event</u> happens that kills them all (e.g. a volcanic eruption or a collision with an asteroid).
- A <u>new species</u> develops (this is called speciation — see below).

> A species is a group of similar organisms that can reproduce to give fertile offspring.

Speciation is the Development of a New Species

1) <u>Speciation</u> is when a <u>new species</u> develops.

2) <u>Isolation</u> is where <u>populations</u> of a species are <u>separated</u>, e.g. due to a <u>physical barrier</u>.

3) Isolation can cause speciation:

- Things like floods and earthquakes can cause barriers that <u>isolate</u> some individuals from the main population.
- <u>Conditions</u> on either side of the barrier will be <u>slightly different</u>, e.g. they may have <u>different climates</u>.
- Because the environment is <u>different</u> on each side, <u>different characteristics</u> will become more common in each population.
- After a very long time, individuals from the different populations will have <u>changed</u> so much that they will have become <u>separate species</u>.

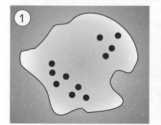
Two populations of the same species
● = individual organism

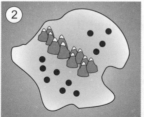
Physical barriers separate populations.

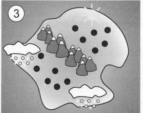
Populations adapt to new environments.

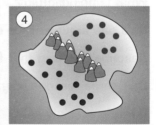
Development of a new species.

Up for grabs — a top quality gag about speciation...going once...going twice...

So... <u>speciation</u> is when a new species develops, caused by the populations becoming <u>separated</u> from each other. Phew. Right, I think it must be nearly time for a <u>tea break</u> before your brain cells become extinct...

Revision Summary for Biology 2b

Wow, that was quite a long section. First there was all the stuff on enzymes and then came all the genetics bits. And just to finish off, some questions. Use these to find out what you know about it all — and what you don't. Then look back and learn the bits you don't know. Then try the questions again, and again...

1) Give a definition of a catalyst.

2) Explain why a reaction involving enzymes stops when the temperature gets too high.

3) Where in the body is bile: a) produced?   b) stored?   c) used?

4) Write down the word equation for aerobic respiration.

5) Give one example of how an animal uses the energy released by aerobic respiration.

6) What is anaerobic respiration?

7) Give one kind of enzyme that would be useful in a biological washing powder.

8) Describe the structure of DNA.

9) What is mitosis used for in the human body?

10) Name the other type of cell division.

11) What is differentiation in a cell?

12) Give one way that stem cells could be used to cure diseases.

13) Which chromosome in the human body causes male characteristics?

14) Copy and complete the diagram to show what happens to the X and Y chromosomes during reproduction.

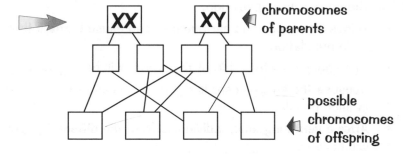

chromosomes of parents

possible chromosomes of offspring

15) What is an allele?

16) List one important conclusion that Mendel reached following his experiments with pea plants.

17) What is polydactyly?

18) Give one argument for embryo screening and one against it.

19) Describe one way that fossils can form.

20) Give three reasons why some species become extinct.

21) What is speciation?

Atoms, Compounds and Isotopes

Atoms are very small. They contain <u>three</u> even smaller particles — <u>protons</u>, <u>neutrons</u> and <u>electrons</u>.

Atomic Number and Mass Number Describe an Atom

Particles are the smallest bits that make up something.

These two numbers tell you how many of each kind of particle an atom has.

The Mass Number ➤ **^{23}Na**
— Total number of protons and neutrons

The Atomic Number ➤ $_{11}$**Na**
— Number of protons

PARTICLE	RELATIVE MASS
Proton	1
Neutron	1
Electron	very small

1) <u>Different</u> elements will have <u>different</u> numbers of <u>protons</u>.

2) To get the number of <u>neutrons</u>, just <u>take away</u> the <u>atomic number</u> from the <u>mass number</u>.

3) Electrons aren't counted in the mass number because their <u>relative mass</u> is very small.

Relative mass just means how heavy a particle is compared to the others.

Compounds Are Chemically Combined

Carbon + Oxygen ➤ Carbon Dioxide

C + OO ➤ O C O

1) Compounds are made when <u>atoms</u> of <u>two or more</u> elements are <u>chemically combined</u> (joined) together.

2) For example, carbon dioxide is a <u>compound</u>. It's made from a <u>chemical reaction</u> between carbon and oxygen.

Isotopes Are the Same Except for the Number of Neutrons

Isotopes are: <u>atoms</u> of the <u>same element</u>, which have the <u>SAME</u> number of <u>PROTONS</u> but a <u>DIFFERENT</u> number of <u>NEUTRONS</u>.

1) <u>If</u> they had <u>different</u> numbers of protons, they'd be <u>different</u> elements.

2) <u>Carbon-12</u> and <u>carbon-14</u> are two isotopes of carbon.

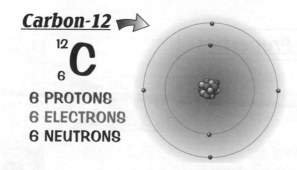

Carbon-12 ➤
$^{12}_{6}$**C**
6 PROTONS
6 ELECTRONS
6 NEUTRONS

Carbon-14 ➤
$^{14}_{6}$**C**
6 PROTONS
6 ELECTRONS
8 NEUTRONS

Will this be in your exam — isotope so...

It's really important you understand that an isotope is just the <u>same element</u> with a different number of <u>neutrons</u>.

Ionic Bonding

Ionic Bonding — Transferring Electrons

1) In ionic bonding, atoms lose or gain electrons to form ions.

2) Ions can have a positive (+) or negative (−) charge.

3) Oppositely charged ions are attracted to each other to form ionic bonds.

A Shell with Just One or Two Electrons Wants to Lose Them...

1) Atoms with just one or two electrons in their outer shell (highest energy level) want to lose these.

2) Then they will have a full shell. This means they will have the same electronic structure as a noble gas.

Noble gases all have full outer shells.

A Nearly Full Shell Wants to Gain Electrons...

1) Atoms with nearly full outer shells want to gain an extra one or two electrons to fill the shell up.

2) So they take an electron (or two) from an atom that wants to lose one (or two).

For example, sodium and chlorine react to make sodium chloride:

The sodium (Na) atom loses its outer electron. It becomes an Na⁺ ion.

The chlorine (Cl) atom has picked up the spare electron. It becomes a Cl⁻ ion.

Ionic Compounds Are a Giant Regular Structure of Ions

1) Ionic compounds have a giant ionic lattice structure.

2) The oppositely charged ions in the compound are attracted to each other. The forces of attraction are called electrostatic forces. They act in all directions between the ions.

3) Sodium chloride (salt) is a giant ionic lattice. The Na⁺ and Cl⁻ ions are held together in a regular lattice.

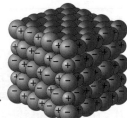

⬤ = Cl⁻
● = Na⁺

Ionic Compounds All Have Similar Properties

1) They all have high melting points and high boiling points. It takes a lot of energy to break the strong bonds.

2) When ionic compounds melt, the ions are free to move. This means they'll carry electric current.

3) Ionic compounds dissolve easily in water. The ions separate and are free to move. This means they'll carry electric current.

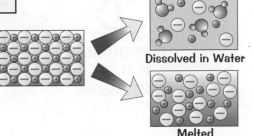

Dissolved in Water

Melted

Giant ionic lattices — all over your chips...

Ionic compounds are hard to melt. But if they do melt, they get all excited and start carrying electric current.

Ions and Formulas

Make sure you really understand the joys of ionic bonding before you start this page.

Groups 1 and 7 Form Ions Easily

1) Atoms that have <u>lost</u> an electron (or electrons) are <u>positively (+) charged ions</u>.

2) Atoms that have <u>gained</u> an electron are <u>negatively (−) charged ions</u>.

3) Ions have the <u>electronic structure</u> of a <u>noble gas</u> (they have a full outer shell).

4) <u>Group 1</u> elements (the <u>alkali metals</u>) are <u>metals</u>.
   - They <u>lose</u> an electron to form an <u>ion</u> with a 1^+ charge.
   - They form ionic compounds with <u>non-metals</u>, e.g. K^+Cl^-.

5) <u>Group 7</u> elements (the <u>halogens</u>) are <u>non-metals</u>.
   - They <u>gain</u> an electron to form an <u>ion</u> with a 1^- charge (a halide ion).
   - They form ionic compounds with the <u>alkali metals</u>, e.g. Na^+Cl^-.

6) <u>Group 1 ions</u> always have a 1^+ charge.

7) <u>Group 7 ions</u> always have a 1^- charge.

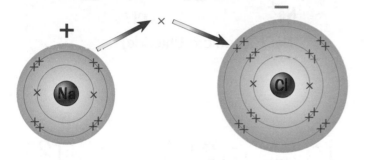

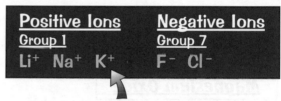

Positive Ions	Negative Ions
Group 1	Group 7
Li^+ Na^+ K^+	F^- Cl^-

Any of these positive ions can combine with any of the negative ions to form an ionic compound.

Look at Charges to Work Out the Formula of an Ionic Compound

1) Ionic compounds are made up of a <u>positively charged</u> part (+) and a <u>negatively charged</u> part (−).

2) The <u>negative</u> charges in the compound must <u>balance out</u> the <u>positive</u> charges. For example, if you've got a 1^- ion there also needs to be a 1^+ ion.

Sodium chloride contains Na^+ (1^+) and Cl^- (1^-) ions.
The charges are already the same (1 and 1) so we only need <u>one</u> of each ion. So the formula for sodium chloride = NaCl.

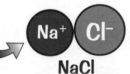

NaCl

Magnesium chloride contains Mg^{2+} (2^+) and Cl^- (1^-) ions.
The charges don't balance (2 and 1). So we will need <u>two</u> Cl^- ions to balance the 2^+ charge of the magnesium ion. This gives us the formula $MgCl_2$.

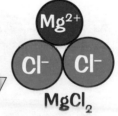

$MgCl_2$

The little 2 after the 'Cl' shows that there are 2 Cl^- ions.

The formula for exam success = revision...

Remember, the + and − charges only appear when an atom <u>reacts</u> with something and becomes an ion.

Electronic Structure of Ions

This page is full of lovely drawings of <u>electronic structures</u>. I hope you're feeling arty.

Show the Electronic Structure of Ions With Drawings

1) To <u>draw</u> the <u>electronic structure</u> of ions, just use a big <u>square bracket</u> and a + or − to show the charge.
2) Remember, the <u>charge</u> on the <u>ion</u> depends on how many <u>electrons</u> the atom has <u>lost</u> or <u>gained</u>.
3) You need to know how to draw the <u>ions</u> and the <u>ionic compounds</u> shown below:

Electronic structures just show all the electrons in their shells.

Sodium Chloride

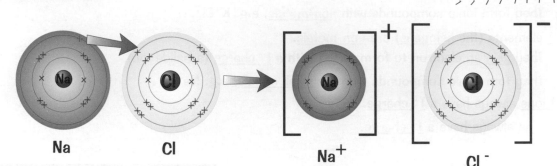

NaCl (Sodium Chloride)

Magnesium Oxide

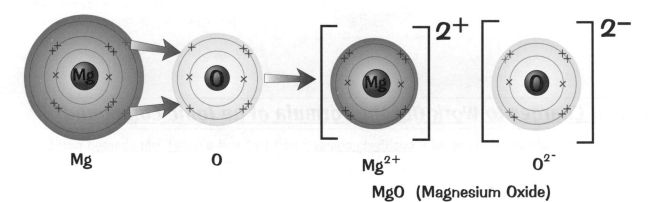

MgO (Magnesium Oxide)

Calcium Chloride

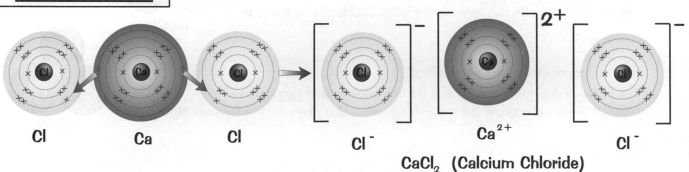

CaCl₂ (Calcium Chloride)

Any old ion, any old ion — any, any, any old ion...

3 ionic compounds, 3 drawings, 1 exam hall. It's like the start of a bad game show. If you don't understand <u>ionic bonding</u> you might find these drawings tricky. (So if you're struggling, try reading the last few pages again.)

Covalent Bonding

Some atoms bond ionically (see page 42) but others form strong <u>covalent bonds</u>.

<u>Covalent Bonds — Sharing Electrons</u>

1) Atoms can make <u>covalent bonds</u> by <u>sharing</u> electrons with other atoms.
2) They only share electrons in their <u>outer shells</u> (highest energy levels).
3) This way <u>both</u> atoms feel that they have a <u>full outer shell</u> (like a noble gas).
4) A covalent bond is a <u>shared pair</u> of electrons.
5) Each atom has to make <u>enough</u> covalent bonds to <u>fill up</u> its outer shell.
6) Covalent bonds between atoms are very <u>strong</u>.

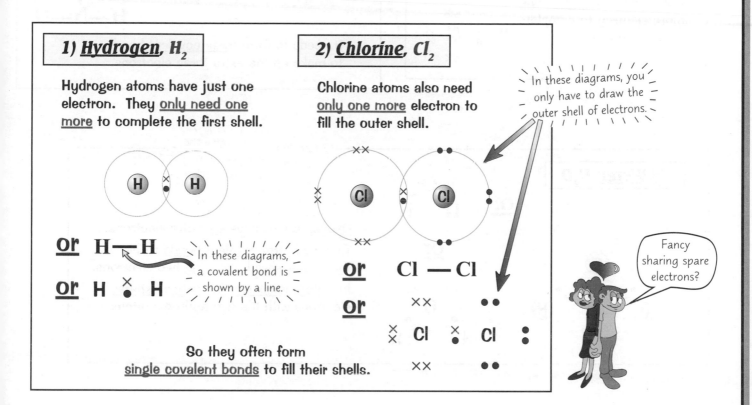

1) <u>Hydrogen</u>, H_2

Hydrogen atoms have just one electron. They <u>only need one more</u> to complete the first shell.

or H — H

or H $\times$ • H

In these diagrams, a covalent bond is shown by a line.

So they often form <u>single covalent bonds</u> to fill their shells.

2) <u>Chlorine</u>, Cl_2

Chlorine atoms also need <u>only one more</u> electron to fill the outer shell.

or Cl — Cl

In these diagrams, you only have to draw the outer shell of electrons.

Fancy sharing spare electrons?

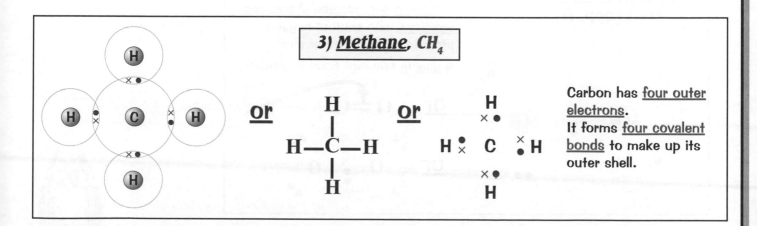

3) <u>Methane</u>, CH_4

or H—C—H (with H top and bottom)

or dot and cross diagram

Carbon has <u>four outer electrons</u>.
It forms <u>four covalent bonds</u> to make up its outer shell.

<u>Covalent bonding — it's good to share...</u>

There are another four covalent bonding diagrams still to come. Make sure you know these first. When you've drawn a dot and cross diagram, count up the number of electrons to <u>double check</u> you've got a full outer shell.

More Covalent Bonding

You lucky thing. Here are the next four diagrams I told you about.

4) Hydrogen Chloride, HCl

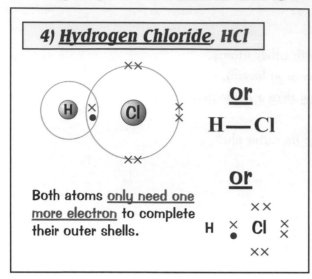

or

H—Cl

or

Both atoms <u>only need one more electron</u> to complete their outer shells.

5) Ammonia, NH₃

Nitrogen has <u>five</u> outer electrons.

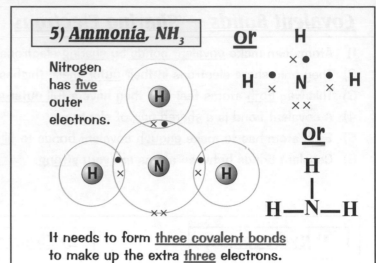

It needs to form <u>three covalent bonds</u> to make up the extra <u>three</u> electrons.

Remember — it's only the outer shells that share electrons with each other.

6) Water, H₂O

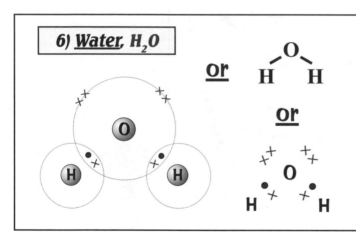

Or

Or

<u>Oxygen</u> atoms have <u>six</u> outer electrons.

They can form <u>covalent bonds</u> to fill their outer shell by <u>sharing</u> two electrons.

In <u>water molecules</u>, the oxygen <u>shares</u> electrons with the two hydrogen atoms.

7) Oxygen, O₂

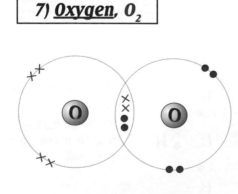

In <u>oxygen gas</u>, oxygen <u>shares two electrons</u> with another oxygen atom to get a full outer shell.

A <u>double</u> covalent bond is formed.

or O=O

A double covalent bond is shown by two lines.

or

The name's Bond, Covalent Bond...

Make sure you learn how to <u>draw</u> these four examples too and understand <u>why they work</u>. Every atom wants a full outer shell. They get that by becoming an <u>ion</u> (see page 42) or by <u>sharing electrons</u>.

Covalent Substances — Two Kinds

Substances with <u>covalent bonds</u> (electron sharing) can be <u>simple molecules</u> or <u>giant structures</u>.

Simple Molecular Substances

1) In simple molecular substances, <u>small molecules</u> with <u>strong</u> covalent bonds are <u>weakly</u> joined together.

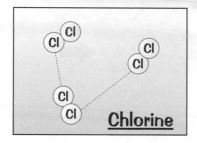
Chlorine

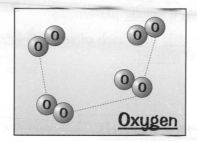
Oxygen

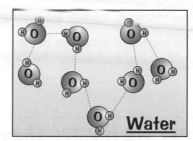
Water

2) Most molecular substances are <u>gases or liquids</u> at room temperature. They can be <u>solids</u> though.
3) Simple molecular substances have <u>low melting points</u> and <u>low boiling points</u>.
4) Molecular substances <u>don't conduct electricity</u>. There are <u>no ions</u> so there's <u>no electrical charge</u>.

Giant Covalent Structures Are Macromolecules

A macromolecule is just a very large molecule.

1) In giant covalent structures, <u>all</u> the atoms are <u>joined</u> to <u>each other</u> by <u>strong</u> covalent bonds.
2) This means that they have <u>very high melting points</u> and <u>very high boiling points</u>.
3) Giant covalent substances <u>don't conduct electricity</u>, except <u>graphite</u>.

Diamond

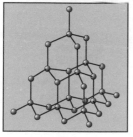

1) Each carbon atom forms <u>four</u> <u>covalent bonds</u> held <u>tightly</u> in a giant covalent structure.
2) This makes diamond very <u>hard</u>.

Silicon Dioxide (Silica)

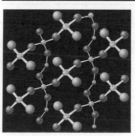

This is a <u>giant structure</u> of silicon and oxygen.

Graphite

Diamond and graphite are both forms of carbon.

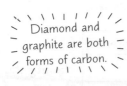
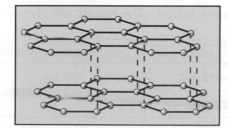

1) Each carbon atom only forms <u>three covalent bonds</u>.
2) This creates <u>layers</u> which are free to <u>slide over each other</u>.
3) This makes graphite <u>soft</u> and <u>slippery</u>.

Carbon is a girl's best friend...

The <u>two different types</u> of covalent substance are very different — make sure you know about them both. You should be able to tell them apart by looking at diagrams of their <u>bonding</u>. Just what you always wanted.

Metals and Identifying Structures

Ever wondered what makes <u>metals</u> tick? Well, either way, you need to learn this page.

Metals Are Regular Structures

1) <u>Metals</u> have <u>giant structures</u>.

2) The atoms in metals are arranged in a <u>regular</u> pattern.

3) The layers of atoms in metals can <u>slide</u> over each other. This means metals can be <u>bent</u> and <u>shaped</u>.

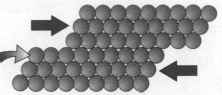

Alloys are Harder Than Pure Metals

1) Two or more <u>different metals</u> can be mixed together to make an <u>alloy</u>.

2) Different metals have <u>different sized atoms</u>.

3) So when one metal is mixed with another, the nice neat layers are <u>messed up</u>.

4) This makes it harder for them to slide over each other. So alloys are <u>harder</u>.

You Can Identify the Structure of a Substance by Its Properties

You should be able to <u>identify</u> most substances as either:

- <u>giant ionic</u> (see page 42),
- <u>simple molecular</u> (see page 47),
- <u>giant covalent</u> (see page 47),

In the exam they might describe the <u>properties</u> of a substance and ask you to decide <u>which type of structure</u> it has. Try this one:

Example: The properties of four substances were tested. The results are shown below:

Substance	Melting point (°C)	Boiling point (°C)	Good electrical conductor?
A	−218.4	−182.96	No
B	1410	2355	No
C	801	1413	When melted

Identify the structure of each substance. (Answers on page 115.)

Alloy, alloy — what do we have here then...

You have to be able to <u>identify</u> the structure of a substance by its properties. Round of Cluedo anyone?

New Materials

New materials with new properties are being developed all the time.

Some Alloys Have Really Weird Properties

1) Nitinol is an example of a "shape memory alloy".

2) When nitinol is cool you can bend it and twist it.

3) But here's the really clever bit — if you heat it above a certain temperature, it goes back to a 'remembered' shape.

4) Nitinol is used for dental braces. In the mouth it warms and tries to return to a 'remembered' shape. It gently pulls the teeth with it.

You met alloys on page 48.

NEXT

Nanoparticles Are Really Really Really Really Tiny

...smaller than that.

1) Nanoparticles are really tiny particles, 1–100 nanometres across (1 nanometre = 0.000 000 001 metres).

2) Nanoparticles contain a few hundred atoms.

3) Nanoparticles have a huge surface area compared to their volume.

4) A nanoparticle has very different properties from the 'bulk' chemical that it's made from. For example, a nanoparticle made from carbon atoms has different properties from a big lump of carbon.

5) Using nanoparticles is known as nanoscience.

6) Many new uses of nanoparticles are being developed:

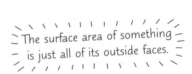

The surface area of something is just all of its outside faces.

- New catalysts (see page 61).

- Sensors that can detect one type of molecule and nothing else.

- Stronger and lighter building materials.

- New cosmetics, e.g. sun tan cream and deodorant.

- New lubricant coatings that reduce friction a bit like ball bearings.

- Tiny electric circuits for computer chips.

Bendy braces, lubricants and computer chips — cool...

Some nanoparticles have really strange properties. This is great news for scientists and inventors. Yay. On the flipside, we also need to watch out for any harmful properties that we don't know about yet.

Polymers

There's plastic and there's... well, plastic. You wouldn't want to make a chair with the same plastic that gets used for flimsy old carrier bags. But whatever the plastic, it's always a polymer.

Thermosoftening and Thermosetting Are Two Types of Polymers

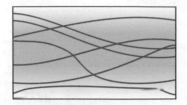

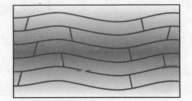

1) THERMOSOFTENING POLYMERS are made up of <u>lots of tangled chains</u> of polymers.

2) These can <u>slide</u> over each other.

3) They're dead easy to <u>melt</u>.

1) THERMOSETTING POLYMERS have <u>crosslinks</u> between the chains of polymers.

2) These hold the chains together in a <u>solid structure</u>.

3) This means the polymer <u>doesn't melt</u> when heated.

How You Make a Polymer Affects Its Properties

1) A polymer's properties depend on <u>what it's made from</u> and the <u>reaction conditions</u> (e.g. temperature).

2) Two types of <u>polythene</u> can be made using <u>different catalysts</u> and <u>different reaction conditions</u>:

• <u>Low density</u> (LD) polythene is <u>flexible</u> and is used for bags and bottles.

• <u>High density</u> (HD) polythene is <u>stiffer</u> and is used for water tanks and drainpipes.

The Use of a Plastic Depends on Its Properties

You might need to answer a question like this one in the exam.

Choose from the table the plastic that would be best suited for making:

a) a throw-away cup for hot drinks,

b) clothing,

c) a measuring cylinder.

Give reasons for each choice.

Plastic	Cost	Is it damaged by chemicals?	Melting point	Is it see-through?	Is it flexible?
W	High	No	High	No	No
X	Low	Yes	Low	No	Yes
Y	High	No	High	Yes	No
Z	Low	Yes	High	Yes	No

<u>Answers</u>

a) Z — low cost (throw-away) and high melting point (for hot drinks),

b) X — flexible (needed for clothing)

c) Y — see-through and not damaged by chemicals (you need to be able to see the liquid inside, and the liquid and measuring cylinder mustn't react with each other).

Credit cards — my favourite sort of plastic...

From pen lids to potties, plastic is everywhere. What each type of plastic is used for is down to its properties.

Relative Formula Mass

The biggest trouble with <u>relative formula mass</u> is that it <u>sounds</u> a lot worse than it really is.

Relative Formula Mass, M_r — Add Up The Relative Atomic Masses, A_r

1) In the periodic table, the <u>elements</u> all have <u>two</u> numbers.
The <u>bigger one</u> is the <u>mass number</u> (see page 41). This number is also the <u>relative atomic mass</u>, A_r.

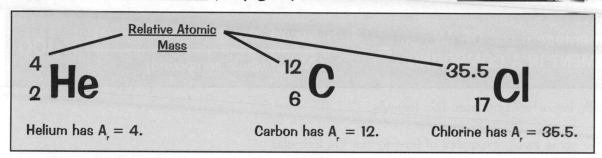

Relative Atomic Mass

$^4_2$He

Helium has $A_r = 4$.

$^{12}_6$C

Carbon has $A_r = 12$.

$^{35.5}_{17}$Cl

Chlorine has $A_r = 35.5$.

2) If you have a <u>compound</u> like $MgCl_2$ then it has a <u>relative formula mass</u>, M_r.
It's just all the relative atomic masses <u>added together</u>.
For $MgCl_2$ it would be:

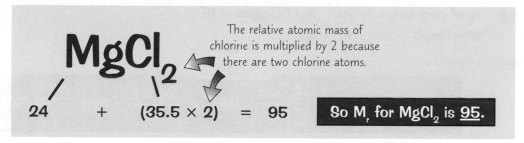

$MgCl_2$

The relative atomic mass of chlorine is multiplied by 2 because there are two chlorine atoms.

$24 \quad + \quad (35.5 \times 2) \quad = \quad 95$

So M_r for $MgCl_2$ is <u>95</u>.

3) You can easily get the relative atomic mass (A_r) for any element from the periodic table
(see inside front cover). But in a lot of questions they give you them anyway.

4) And that's all it is. A big fancy name like <u>relative formula mass</u> and it just means
"<u>add up all the relative atomic masses</u>". What a swizz.

"ONE MOLE" of a Substance is Equal to its M_r or A_r in Grams

The <u>relative formula mass</u> (M_r) or <u>relative atomic mass</u> (A_r) of a
substance <u>in grams</u> is known as <u>one mole</u> of that substance.

<u>Examples</u>:

Iron, Fe, has an A_r of 56.

Nitrogen gas, N_2, has an M_r of 28 (2×14).

Potassium chloride, KCl, has an M_r of 74.5 ($39 + 35.5$).

So one mole of iron weighs exactly 56 g

So one mole of N_2 weighs exactly 28 g

So one mole of KCl weighs exactly 74.5 g

Numbers? — and you thought you were doing chemistry...

Read through the stuff on this page about how to work out <u>relative formula mass</u>. Then, have a go at these:
Find the relative formula mass of: NaOH, Fe_2O_3, C_6H_{14}
Here are the relative atomic masses: Na=23, O=16, Fe=56, C=12, H=1.   Answers on page 115

Calculating Percentage Mass

The calculation on this page uses <u>relative atomic mass</u>, A_r, and <u>relative formula mass</u>, M_r. So, if you're not sure what they are, you'll need to turn back a page and read it again. There's no way round it.

Calculating Percentage Mass of an Element in a Compound

Here's the magic formula:

$$\text{Percentage mass OF AN ELEMENT IN A COMPOUND} = \frac{A_r \times \text{No. of atoms (of that element)}}{M_r \text{ (of whole compound)}} \times 100$$

It's really important you learn this formula.

Here are some lovely examples of how to use the formula:

<u>EXAMPLE:</u> Find the percentage mass of magnesium in magnesium oxide, MgO.

<u>ANSWER:</u> A_r of magnesium = 24, A_r of oxygen = 16
  M_r of MgO = 24 + 16 = 40

'n' is just short for number.

Now use the formula:

$$\underline{\text{Percentage mass}} = \frac{A_r \times n}{M_r} \times 100 = \frac{24 \times 1}{40} \times 100 = 60\%$$

And there you have it. Magnesium makes up <u>60%</u> of the mass of magnesium oxide.

<u>EXAMPLE:</u> Find the percentage mass of sodium in sodium carbonate, Na_2CO_3.

<u>ANSWER:</u> A_r of sodium = 23, A_r of carbon = 12, A_r of oxygen = 16
  M_r of Na_2CO_3 = (2 × 23) + 12 + (3 × 16) = 106

Now use the formula:

$$\underline{\text{Percentage mass}} = \frac{A_r \times n}{M_r} \times 100 = \frac{23 \times 2}{106} \times 100 = 43.4\%$$

So sodium makes up <u>43.4%</u> of the mass of sodium carbonate. The end.

I like to think of my percentage mass as 10% pig, 90% feathers...

So, like I said before, you really do need to know the <u>formula</u> for working out percentage mass. It's written all over the page, so no excuses. Now here are some practice questions:
Find the percentage mass of oxygen in each of these: a) Fe_2O_3 b) H_2O c) $CaCO_3$ Answers on page 115

Percentage Yield and Reversible Reactions

Percentage yield tells you how well an experiment worked.

Percentage Yield Compares Actual and Expected Yield

The amount of product you get from a reaction is called the yield.

1) Chemists can work out what yield they'd expect to get from a reaction.
2) But in real life the actual yield is always lower than expected.
3) Percentage yield compares the amount of product chemists really get with what they expected to get.
4) Percentage yield is always somewhere between 0 and 100%.
5) A 100% yield means that all the expected product was made.
6) A 0% yield means that no product was made.

Yields Are Always Less Than 100%

Even though no atoms are gained or lost in reactions, you never get all the product you'd expect.
So you never get a 100% yield. There are several reasons for this:

1) The reaction is reversible:

A reversible reaction is one where the products of the reaction can react and turn back into the reactants.

$$A + B \rightleftharpoons C + D$$

So C and D can react to produce A and B.

For example:
ammonium chloride $\rightleftharpoons$ ammonia + hydrogen chloride

Some of the products are always reacting together to turn back into reactants. So the yield will be lower.

2) When you filter a liquid to remove a solid, you always lose a bit of liquid or a bit of solid.
So, some of the product may be lost when it's separated from the reaction mixture.

3) Sometimes there can be other unexpected reactions happening. These will use up the reactants.
This means there's not as much reactant to make the product you want.

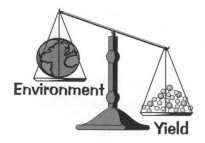
Environment — Yield

1) Thinking about yield is important for sustainable development.
2) Sustainable development is about making sure that we don't use resources faster than they can be replaced. We need to leave some for people in the future.
3) We should aim to:
   - use as little energy as we can.
   - use as few reactants as we can.
   - get the highest yield we can.

You can't always get what you want...

A high percentage yield means there's not much waste — which is good for saving resources.
If a reaction's going to be worth doing, it normally has to have a high percentage yield.

Chemical Analysis and Instrumental Methods

There are some pretty clever ways of <u>identifying</u> substances, from using filter paper to machines...

Artificial Colours Can Be Separated Using Paper Chromatography

A <u>food colouring</u> might contain <u>one dye</u> or it might be a <u>mixture of dyes</u>. Here's how you can tell:

1) To get the <u>colour</u> out of a food sample, put it in a cup with a few drops of <u>solvent</u> (e.g. water, ethanol).

2) Draw a line in <u>pencil</u> near the bottom of some filter paper.

3) Put a <u>spot</u> of the coloured solution on the line.

4) Roll up the sheet and put it in a <u>beaker</u> with some <u>solvent</u>.

5) The solvent <u>soaks</u> up the paper, taking the dyes with it. Different dyes form spots in <u>different places</u>.

6) You can <u>compare</u> the results against the results from <u>known</u> food colourings to <u>identify</u> the dyes.

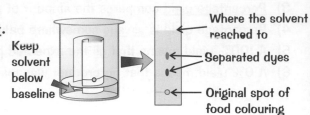

Keep solvent below baseline

Where the solvent reached to

Separated dyes

Original spot of food colouring

Machines Can Identify Elements and Compounds

You can identify substances using <u>instrumental methods</u> — this just means using machines.

Advantages of Using Machines

- <u>Very sensitive</u> — can detect even the <u>tiniest amounts</u>.
- <u>Very fast</u>
- <u>Very accurate</u> — don't make mistakes.

Gas Chromatography Can be Used to Identify Compounds

Gas chromatography can <u>separate out</u> a mixture of compounds and help you <u>identify</u> them.

1) A <u>gas</u> is used to <u>carry</u> substances through a <u>column</u> packed with a <u>solid material</u>.

2) The substances travel through the tube at <u>different speeds</u>, so they're <u>separated</u>.

3) The time they take to reach the <u>detector</u> is called the <u>retention time</u>. It can be used to help <u>identify</u> the substances.

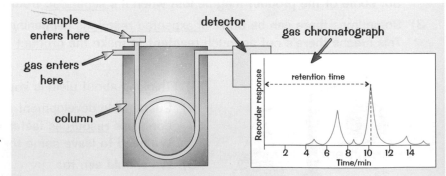

sample enters here

gas enters here

column

detector

gas chromatograph

retention time

Recorder response

Time/min

4) The recorder draws a <u>gas chromatograph</u>.

5) The number of <u>peaks</u> shows the number of <u>different compounds</u> in the sample.

6) The <u>position of the peaks</u> shows the <u>retention time</u> of each substance.

7) The gas chromatography column can also be linked to a machine called a <u>mass spectrometer</u>. This is known as <u>GC-MS</u>. It can identify the substances leaving the column very <u>accurately</u>.

Unfortunately, machines can't do the exam for you...

Make sure you don't get the two types of chromatography muddled up... there's <u>paper</u> and then there's <u>gas</u>.

Revision Summary for Chemistry 2a

Some people skip these pages. But what's the point in reading that great big section if you're not going to check if you really know it or not? Look, just read the first ten questions, and I promise there'll be an answer you'll have to look up. And when it comes up in the exam, you'll be so glad you did.

1) What does the mass number tell you about an atom?

2) Draw a table showing the relative masses of a proton, neutron and electron.

3) What is a compound?

4) What is an isotope?

5) What happens in ionic bonding?

6) Describe the structure of sodium chloride.

7) List the main properties of ionic compounds.

8) What type of ion do elements from the following groups form?
   a) Group 1   b) Group 7

9)* Work out the formulas of these ionic compounds: Potassium ion = K^+, Calcium ion = Ca^{2+},
   a) potassium chloride   b) calcium chloride   Chloride ion = Cl^-

10)* Draw a diagram to show the electronic structure of an Mg^{2+} ion (magnesium's atomic number is 12).

11) What is covalent bonding?

12) Sketch a diagram showing the bonding in molecules of:
   a) hydrogen   b) hydrogen chloride

13) What are the two types of covalent substance? Give three examples of each.

14) Explain why alloys are harder than pure metals.

15)* Identify the structure of each of the substances in the table:

Substance	Melting point (°C)	Electrical conductivity	Hardness
A	101	Zero	Soft
B	2072	Zero	Very Hard
C	605	Zero when solid High when melted	Soft

16) What is special about nitinol? What is it used for?

17) What are nanoparticles? Give two different uses of nanoparticles.

18) Explain the difference between thermosoftening and thermosetting polymers.

19)* Find A_r or M_r for these (use the periodic table at the front of the book):
   a) Ca   b) Ag   c) CO_2 d) $MgCO_3$

20) What is the link between moles and relative formula mass?

21)* Calculate the percentage mass of carbon in: a) $CaCO_3$ b) CO_2 c) CH_4

22) Give three reasons that the percentage yield of a reaction is never 100%.

23) Explain how paper chromatography can be used to identify the dyes used in a brown sweet.

24) Briefly describe how gas chromatography works.

* Answers on page 115

Chemistry 2a — Bonding and Calculations

Rate of Reaction

As a reaction happens a <u>product</u> is made. The <u>rate of a reaction</u> is just how fast the product is made.

The Rate of a Reaction Depends on Four Things:

1) <u>Temperature</u>
2) <u>Concentration</u> (or <u>pressure</u> for gases)
3) <u>Catalyst</u>
4) <u>Surface area of solids</u> (or <u>size</u> of solid pieces)

LEARN THEM!

The Rate of a Reaction Can Be Shown on a Graph

1) The graph below shows how the rate of a reaction can change.

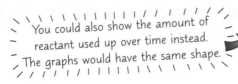
You could also show the amount of reactant used up over time instead. The graphs would have the same shape.

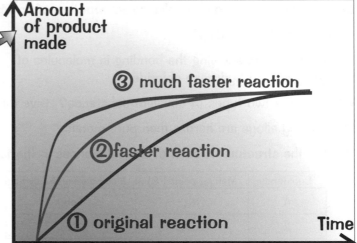

2) The <u>quickest reaction</u> is shown by the line with the <u>steepest slope</u>.

3) Also, the <u>faster</u> a reaction goes, the <u>sooner</u> it finishes.

4) When the reaction finishes, <u>no more product</u> is made. So the line goes <u>flat</u>.

5) So in a <u>faster</u> reaction the line becomes <u>flat</u> earlier.

1) <u>Graph 1</u> shows a <u>fairly slow</u> reaction. The graph isn't too steep.

2) <u>Graphs 2 and 3</u> show the reaction taking place <u>faster</u>. The slope of the graphs gets steeper.

3) The <u>increased rate</u> could be due to <u>any</u> of these:

> a) increase in <u>temperature</u>
> b) increase in <u>concentration</u> (or <u>pressure</u>)
> c) <u>catalyst</u> added
> d) <u>smaller bits</u> of reactant (<u>larger surface area</u>)

4) <u>Graphs 1, 2 and 3</u> all start with the same amount of reactants. So they all become flat at the same level as they all make the same amount of product. They just take <u>different</u> times to get there.

Get a fast reaction — tickle your brother...

Not all reactions go at the same rate. You need to know what four things can change the <u>rate of a reaction</u>.

Measuring Rates of Reaction

Ways to Measure the Rate of a Reaction

1) The rate of a reaction can be found by measuring one of these two things:

   - how quickly the reactants are used up
   - how quickly the products are formed

2) The rate of a reaction can be worked out using this formula:

$$\text{Rate of Reaction} = \frac{\text{Amount of reactant used}}{\text{Time}} \quad \text{OR} \quad \frac{\text{Amount of product formed}}{\text{Time}}$$

3) There are different ways that the rate of a reaction can be measured. Learn these three:

1) Precipitation

1) This is when the product of the reaction is a precipitate (solid) which makes the solution cloudy.

2) Watch a mark through the solution and time how long it takes to disappear.

3) The quicker the mark disappears, the quicker the reaction.

4) This only works for reactions that start with a see-through solution.

2) Change in Mass (Usually Gas Given Off)

1) Measure the amount of gas given off by a reaction using a mass balance.

2) The mass will drop as gas is given off.

3) The quicker the reading on the balance drops, the faster the reaction.

3) The Volume of Gas Given Off

1) Use a gas syringe to measure the volume of gas given off.

2) The more gas given off in a set time, the faster the reaction.

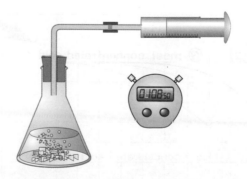

OK have you got your stopwatch ready *BANG!* — oh...

Each method has its pros and cons. The first method isn't very accurate. But if you're not producing a gas you can't use either of the other two. Ah well. You might need to choose a method in the exam so learn all three.

Rate of Reaction Experiments

Here are four different reactions. Each tests one of the things that can affect the <u>rate</u> of a reaction. Enjoy.

Reaction of Hydrochloric Acid (HCl) and Marble Chips

1) Measure the <u>volume</u> of gas given off with a <u>gas syringe</u>.
2) Take readings at <u>regular</u> times (e.g. every 10 seconds).
3) <u>Repeat</u> the experiment with <u>smaller marble</u> chips. Then repeat it with <u>powdered marble</u>.
4) Use <u>exactly the same</u> mass of marble and volume of <u>acid</u> each time.
5) If you plot your readings on a graph, it will look something like this:

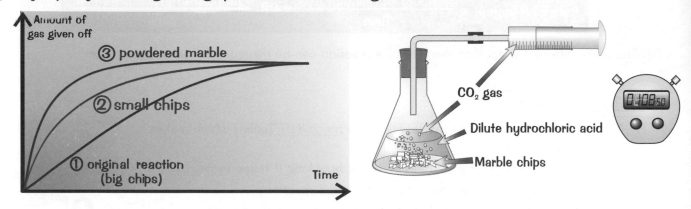

- Using <u>smaller bits</u> gives the marble a <u>larger surface area</u>.
- A <u>larger</u> surface area gives a <u>steeper</u> graph with the reaction finishing <u>quicker</u>.

Reaction of Magnesium Metal with Dilute Hydrochloric Acid

1) This reaction gives off <u>hydrogen gas</u>. The loss of the gas can be measured with a <u>mass balance</u>.
2) Take <u>readings</u> at <u>regular</u> times (e.g. every 10 seconds).
3) Work out the <u>loss in mass</u> for each reading (take away the reading from the starting mass).
4) <u>Repeat</u> with <u>more concentrated</u> acid solutions.
5) Keep the <u>volume</u> of acid and <u>amount</u> of magnesium <u>the same</u> each time.
6) A <u>higher</u> concentration gives a <u>steeper graph</u>, with the reaction <u>finishing</u> quicker.

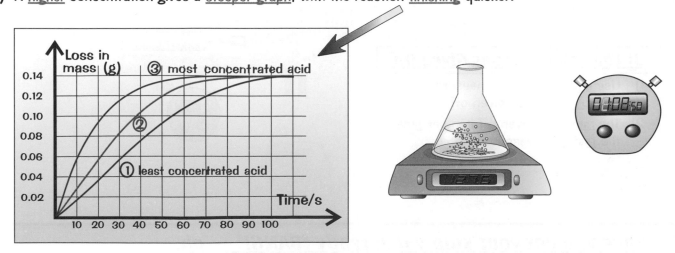

More Rate of Reaction Experiments

Sodium Thiosulfate and HCl Give a Cloudy Precipitate

1) These two chemicals are both <u>clear solutions</u>.

2) They react together to form a <u>yellow precipitate</u> of <u>sulfur</u>.

3) Watch a black mark through the <u>cloudy sulfur</u> and <u>time</u> how long it takes until you <u>can't see it</u> anymore.

> A precipitate is a solid that forms in a solution.

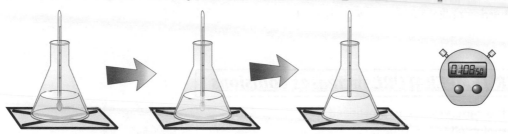

4) The reaction can be <u>repeated</u> for solutions at different <u>temperatures</u>.

5) The <u>volume</u> of liquid must be kept the <u>same</u> each time.

6) The <u>higher</u> the temperature the <u>less time</u> it'll take for the mark to <u>disappear</u>. This means the reaction is faster.

For example:

Temperature (°C)	20	25	30	35	40
Time taken for mark to disappear (s)	193	151	112	87	52

The Decomposition of Hydrogen Peroxide

1) The decomposition (breaking down) of hydrogen peroxide is normally quite <u>slow</u>.

2) A <u>catalyst</u> can speed it up. Different catalysts can be used.

3) <u>Oxygen gas</u> is given off. So the rate of reaction can be measured using a <u>gas syringe</u>.

4) <u>Better</u> catalysts give a <u>quicker reaction</u>. This is shown by a <u>steeper graph</u> which flattens out quickly.

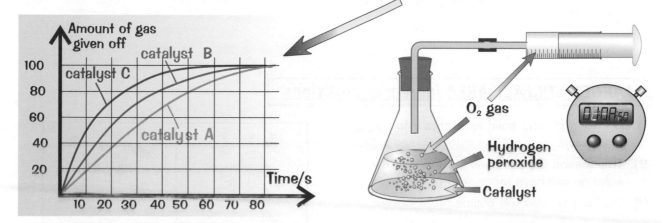

Time flies when a reaction's enjoying itself...

You <u>don't</u> need to know all the details of the reactions on these pages. But you <u>do</u> need to be able to look at graphs or results and comment on the reaction rate. Remember, steeper graphs = faster reactions.

Collisions

I get sort of grumpy if someone bangs into me. But particles have to <u>collide</u> (bang into each other) to <u>react</u>.

More Collisions Increases the Rate of Reaction

1) The <u>rate of reaction</u> can be <u>explained</u> by the collisions between particles.
2) <u>How hard</u> and <u>how often</u> the particles collide affects the rate of reaction.
3) <u>More</u> and <u>harder</u> collisions mean a <u>faster</u> rate.

1) HIGHER TEMPERATURE increases collisions

1) When the <u>temperature is increased</u> the particles all <u>move quicker</u>.
2) If they're moving quicker, they will <u>collide more often</u>.

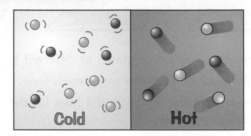

Cold   Hot

2) HIGHER CONCENTRATION (or PRESSURE) increases collisions

1) If a solution is made more <u>concentrated</u> it means there are more particles of <u>reactant</u>.
2) In a <u>gas</u>, increasing the <u>pressure</u> means the particles are <u>more squashed up</u> together.
3) So the particles will collide <u>more often</u>.

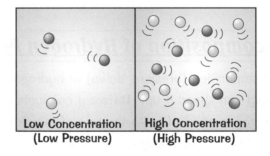

Low Concentration   High Concentration
(Low Pressure)   (High Pressure)

3) LARGER SURFACE AREA increases collisions

1) <u>Breaking up</u> any solid reactants into <u>smaller</u> pieces will <u>increase the total surface area</u>.
2) This means the particles around it in the solution will have <u>more area to hit</u>.
3) So the particles will collide <u>more often</u>.

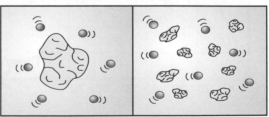

Small surface area   Big surface area

Collision theory — the lamppost ran into me...

The <u>more often</u> particles bump into each other, and the <u>harder</u> they hit when they do, the <u>faster</u> the reaction rate.

Chemistry 2b — Reaction Rates, Salts and Electrolysis

Collisions and Catalysts

On this fine page, prepare yourself to learn about the magic of <u>catalysts</u>. But first, a bit more on <u>collisions</u>...

Faster Collisions Increase the Rate of Reaction

1) <u>Higher temperature</u> makes all the particles <u>move faster</u>. This increases the <u>energy</u> of the collisions.

Increasing the temperature causes faster collisions

2) Reactions <u>only happen</u> if the particles collide with <u>enough energy</u>.

3) The <u>smallest amount</u> of energy that the particles need to react is known as the <u>activation energy</u>.

4) At a higher temperature <u>more particles</u> will collide with <u>enough energy</u> to make the reaction happen.

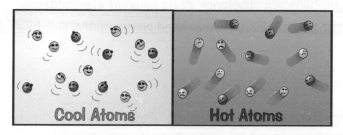

Catalysts Speed Up Reactions

1) Many reactions can be <u>speeded up</u> by adding a <u>catalyst</u>.

> A <u>catalyst</u> is a substance which <u>speeds up</u> a reaction, without being <u>used up</u> in the reaction.

2) Different reactions need different <u>catalysts</u>.
   For example, the Haber process for making ammonia uses an iron catalyst.

Using Catalysts in Industry Has Advantages and Disadvantages

ADVANTAGES:

- Most <u>industrial</u> reactions use catalysts to <u>increase</u> the rate of reaction. This means it takes <u>less time</u> to make the <u>same amount</u> of stuff. This saves a lot of <u>money</u>.
- A catalyst also lets the reaction be done at a <u>much lower temperature</u>. This means less <u>energy</u> is needed which is good for the <u>environment</u>.
- Catalysts never get <u>used up</u>. You can use them <u>over and over</u> again.

DISADVANTAGES:

- Catalysts can be very <u>expensive</u> to <u>buy</u>.
- They often need to be removed and <u>cleaned</u>.
- They can be 'poisoned' by other substances, so they <u>stop working</u>.

Catalysts are like great jokes — they can be used over and over...

Catalysts sound almost too good to be true but there are some <u>bad points</u>. You need to learn them. Sorry.

Energy Transfer in Reactions

Whenever chemical reactions occur, energy is transferred (moved) to or from the surroundings.

In an Exothermic Reaction, Heat is Given Out

An EXOTHERMIC reaction is one which gives out energy to the surroundings.

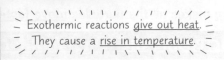
Exothermic reactions give out heat. They cause a rise in temperature.

1) The best example of an exothermic reaction is combustion (burning). This gives out a lot of heat.
2) Neutralisation reactions (acid + alkali) are also exothermic — see page 63.
3) Many oxidation reactions (where a substance gains oxygen) are exothermic.
4) Everyday uses of exothermic reactions include hand warmers and self-heating cans of coffee.

In an Endothermic Reaction, Heat is Taken In

An ENDOTHERMIC reaction is one which takes in energy from the surroundings.

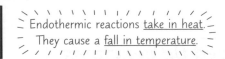
Endothermic reactions take in heat. They cause a fall in temperature.

1) A thermal decomposition reaction (breaking down in heat) is an example of an endothermic reaction.
2) Everyday uses of endothermic reactions include sports injury packs. They take in heat and get very cold.

Reversible Reactions Can Be Endothermic and Exothermic

1) In reversible reactions (see page 53), if the reaction is endothermic in one way, it will be exothermic the other way.
2) The energy taken in by the endothermic reaction is the same as the energy given out during the exothermic reaction. A good example is the thermal decomposition of copper(II) sulfate crystals:

1) Heat blue copper(II) sulfate crystals to remove the water. This leaves white copper(II) sulfate powder. This is endothermic.

2) Add water to the white powder to get the blue crystals back again. This is exothermic.

Water vapour

endothermic

hydrated copper sulfate ⇌ anhydrous copper sulfate + water

exothermic

"Anhydrous" just means "without water", and "hydrated" means "with water".

Energy transfer — make sure you take it all in...

Don't be put off by the long words. Try this: "exo-" = exit, so an exothermic reaction is one that gives out heat.

Acids and Alkalis

Testing the pH of a solution means using an <u>indicator</u> — and that means pretty <u>colours</u>...

The pH Scale Goes From 0 to 14

1) The <u>pH scale</u> is a measure of how <u>acidic</u> or <u>alkaline</u> a solution is.

2) The <u>strongest acid</u> has <u>pH 0</u>. The <u>strongest alkali</u> has <u>pH 14</u>.

3) A <u>neutral</u> substance has <u>pH 7</u> (e.g. pure water).

pH 0   1   2   3   4   5   6   7   8   9   10   11   12   13   14

← ————————— ACIDS ————————— | ————————— ALKALIS ————————— →

NEUTRAL
pure water

4) <u>Indicators</u> are useful for <u>testing</u> the pH of a solution. They <u>change colour</u> at different pHs.

Acids and Bases Neutralise Each Other

1) An <u>ACID</u> has a pH of less than 7. Acids form <u>hydrogen ions</u> (H^+) in <u>water</u>.

2) A <u>BASE</u> has a pH of greater than 7.

3) An <u>ALKALI</u> is a base that <u>dissolves in water</u>. Alkalis form <u>hydroxide ions</u> (OH^-) in <u>water</u>.

4) So, <u>H^+</u> ions make solutions <u>acidic</u>. <u>OH^-</u> ions make them <u>alkaline</u>.

1) The reaction between acids and bases is called <u>neutralisation</u>. Make sure you learn it:

$$acid \ + \ base \ \rightarrow \ salt \ + \ water$$

2) This equation shows what happens to the <u>H^+</u> and <u>OH^-</u> ions during neutralisation:

$$H^+_{(aq)} \ + \ OH^-_{(aq)} \ \rightarrow \ H_2O_{(l)}$$

Hydrogen (H^+) ions react with hydroxide (OH^-) ions to make water (H_2O).

3) When an <u>acid</u> neutralises a <u>base</u> (or a base neutralises an acid), the <u>products</u> are <u>neutral</u> (<u>pH 7</u>).

4) An <u>indicator</u> can be used to show that a neutralisation reaction is <u>over</u> (Universal indicator will go green).

State Symbols Tell You What Physical State It's In

You'll see state symbols in equations. <u>Make sure you know them.</u>

(s) — Solid   (l) — Liquid   (g) — Gas   (aq) — Dissolved in water

Interesting(ish) fact — your skin is slightly acidic (pH 5.5)...

Remember, <u>hydrogen</u> ions (H^+) make solutions <u>acidic</u>. <u>Hydroxide</u> ions (OH^-) make solutions <u>alkaline</u>.

Acids Reacting With Metals

Sadly, the <u>salts</u> on this page aren't the sort you'd want to go putting on your fish and chips.

Metals *React* With Acids to Give *Salts*

Acid + Metal → Salt + Hydrogen

Here's the <u>typical experiment</u>:

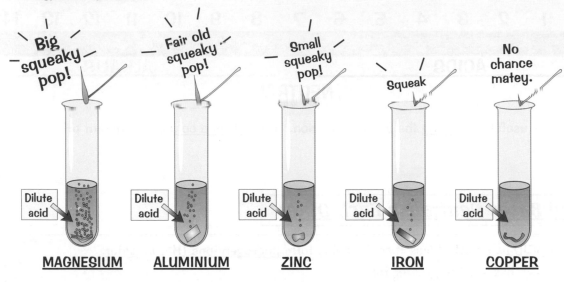

1) The more <u>reactive</u> the metal, the <u>faster</u> the reaction will go.
2) Very reactive metals (e.g. sodium) react <u>explosively</u>.
3) <u>Copper</u> does <u>not</u> react with dilute acids <u>at all</u>.
4) The <u>rate</u> of reaction is shown by how fast the <u>bubbles</u> of hydrogen are given off.
5) You can test for <u>hydrogen</u> using the <u>burning splint test</u>. It will give a '<u>squeaky pop</u>'.
6) The <u>salt</u> made depends on which <u>metal</u> is used, and which <u>acid</u> is used:

Hydrochloric Acid Will Always Make Chloride Salts:

hydrochloric acid + magnesium → magnesium chloride + hydrogen
hydrochloric acid + aluminium → aluminium chloride + hydrogen
hydrochloric acid + zinc → zinc chloride + hydrogen

Sulfuric Acid Will Always Make Sulfate Salts:

sulfuric acid + magnesium → magnesium sulfate + hydrogen
sulfuric acid + aluminium → aluminium sulfate + hydrogen
sulfuric acid + zinc → zinc sulfate + hydrogen

Come on big guy. I'm going to turn you into salt.

Metal and acid — strange ingredients for bubble and squeak...

Some metals <u>don't really react</u> with acids at all. You'd be waiting all day. Other metals like sodium and potassium are <u>too</u> reactive to mix with acid in a school lab — your beaker would <u>explode</u>. Not the best plan.

Oxides, Hydroxides and Ammonia

I'm afraid there's more stuff on <u>neutralisation</u> reactions coming up...

Metal Oxides and Metal Hydroxides Are Bases

1) <u>Metal oxides</u> and <u>metal hydroxides</u> are <u>bases</u>.
2) The ones that <u>dissolve in water</u> are <u>alkalis</u>.
3) All <u>metal oxides</u> and <u>metal hydroxides</u> react with <u>acids</u> to form a <u>salt</u> and <u>water</u>.

$$\text{Acid} + \text{Metal Oxide} \rightarrow \text{Salt} + \text{Water}$$

$$\text{Acid} + \text{Metal Hydroxide} \rightarrow \text{Salt} + \text{Water}$$

These are neutralisation reactions.

The Type of Metal and Acid Decides the Salt

The <u>salt</u> made depends on the <u>acid</u> used and the <u>metal</u> in the base or alkali:

hydrochloric acid	+	copper oxide	→	copper chloride	+ water
hydrochloric acid	+	sodium hydroxide	→	sodium chloride	+ water
sulfuric acid	+	zinc oxide	→	zinc sulfate	+ water
sulfuric acid	+	calcium hydroxide	→	calcium sulfate	+ water
nitric acid	+	magnesium oxide	→	magnesium nitrate	+ water
nitric acid	+	potassium hydroxide	→	potassium nitrate	+ water

Ammonia Can Be Neutralised with Nitric Acid to Make Fertiliser

1) <u>Ammonia</u> dissolves in water to make an <u>alkaline solution</u>.
2) This can be reacted with <u>acid</u> to produce an <u>ammonium salt</u>.

For example: $$\text{ammonia} + \text{nitric acid} \rightarrow \text{ammonium nitrate}$$

This is a bit different from most neutralisation reactions because there's <u>NO WATER</u> produced — just the ammonium salt.

3) <u>Ammonium salts</u> are good fertilisers (plant food).

Ammonium salts? What's wrong with a nice pile of cow poo...

Try working out what salts you'd get by putting different acids and alkalis together. Cover the page and scribble all the equations down. If you make any mistakes... <u>learn</u> it, <u>cover</u> it up, and <u>scribble</u> it all down again.

Chemistry 2b — Reaction Rates, Salts and Electrolysis

Making Salts

Most <u>chloride</u>, <u>sulfate</u> and <u>nitrate</u> salts are <u>soluble</u> in water (but lead chloride, lead sulfate and silver chloride aren't). Most <u>oxides</u> and <u>hydroxides</u> are <u>insoluble</u> in water.

<u>Soluble</u> means it'll <u>dissolve</u>. <u>Insoluble</u> means it <u>won't</u> dissolve.

Making Soluble Salts Using a Metal or an Insoluble Base

1) Pick the right <u>acid</u>, plus a <u>metal</u> or an <u>insoluble base</u> (a <u>metal oxide</u> or <u>metal hydroxide</u>). E.g. to make <u>copper chloride</u>, mix <u>hydrochloric acid</u> and <u>copper oxide</u>:

> copper oxide + hydrochloric acid ⟶ copper chloride + water

filter paper

filter funnel

2) Add the <u>metal</u>, <u>metal oxide</u> or <u>hydroxide</u> to the <u>acid</u> until excess (left over) solid <u>sinks</u> to the bottom of the flask.

3) <u>Filter</u> out the <u>excess</u> solid to get the <u>salt solution</u>. To make <u>crystals</u> of the <u>salt</u>, heat the solution to drive off some of the water.

4) Then leave the rest to dry out very <u>slowly</u>. This is called <u>crystallisation</u>.

Making Soluble Salts Using an Alkali

1) You can't use the method above with <u>alkalis</u> (soluble bases). You can't just add a load of it and filter out what's left because it's <u>soluble</u>.

2) So, add the alkali <u>bit by bit</u> to exactly <u>neutralise</u> the acid — you need to use an <u>indicator</u> (see page 63) to show when the reaction's finished.

3) Then <u>repeat</u> using exactly the same volumes of alkali and acid so the salt <u>isn't mixed with</u> any indicator.

4) <u>Heat</u> to drive off some of the water and leave to <u>dry</u> to <u>crystallise</u> the salt as normal.

Making Insoluble Salts — Precipitation Reactions

1) To make an <u>insoluble</u> salt use a <u>precipitation reaction</u>.

2) Pick <u>two solutions</u> that contain the <u>ions</u> you need. E.g. to make <u>lead chloride</u> you need a solution which contains <u>lead ions</u> and one which contains <u>chloride ions</u>.

3) So you can mix <u>lead nitrate solution</u> with <u>sodium chloride solution</u>:

> lead nitrate + sodium chloride ⟶ lead chloride + sodium nitrate

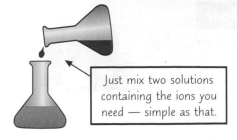

Just mix two solutions containing the ions you need — simple as that.

4) The salt will precipitate out (form as a solid). <u>Filter</u> it from the solution, <u>wash</u> it and then <u>dry</u> it on filter paper.

5) <u>Precipitation reactions</u> can be used to remove <u>unwanted ions</u> from <u>drinking water</u> — e.g. lead ions (which are poisonous).

6) Another use of precipitation is in <u>treating effluent</u> (sewage).

Salt of the earth, of the sea, and of the test tube...

It's a pain but if you're making a salt you need to know if it's soluble or not, so you know which <u>method</u> to use.

Electrolysis

Hmm, electrolysis. A boring title for quite a sparky subject...

Electrolysis Means "Splitting Up with Electricity"

sodium chloride dissolved

1) When an ionic substance is molten (melted) or dissolved, the ions are free to move about in the liquid or solution.

2) These free ions let the liquid or solution conduct electricity.

3) If you pass an electric current through an ionic substance that's molten or in solution, it breaks down into the elements it's made of.

4) This is called electrolysis.

5) The substance that's broken down is called the electrolyte.

molten sodium chloride

Electrolysis Reactions Involve Oxidation and Reduction

1) Reduction is a gain of electrons.

2) Oxidation is a loss of electrons.

3) Electrolysis ALWAYS involves an oxidation and a reduction.

Oxidation	Reduction
Is	Is
Loss of electrons	Gain of electrons

Remember it as OIL RIG.

The Electrolysis of Molten Lead Bromide

If you pass an electric current through molten lead bromide it breaks down into lead and bromine.

Negative Electrode

Positive Electrode

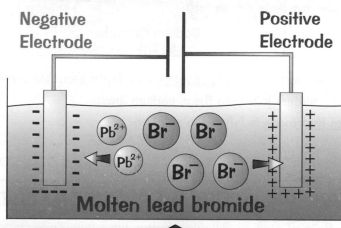

Positive ions move to the negative electrode. Here they gain electrons (reduction).

Lead is produced.

Negative ions move to the positive electrode. Here they lose electrons (oxidation).

Bromine is produced.

Molten lead bromide

HEAT

Faster shopping at Tesco — use Electrolleys...

Learn the products of the electrolysis of molten lead bromide. Make sure you know which is oxidation and which is reduction. Electrolysis is used lots in real life, and it's nice to know how these things work, I think.

Electrolysis of Sodium Chloride Solution

Electrolysis works on <u>solutions</u> as well as <u>molten substances</u>. But first, a bit more about the <u>products</u>...

Reactivity Affects the Products Formed By Electrolysis

1) If an ionic compound is <u>dissolved in water</u>, there'll be ions from the <u>compound</u> and ions from the <u>water</u>.

2) For the electrolysis of <u>solutions</u>, use these <u>rules</u> to help you <u>predict the products</u>.

<u>NEGATIVE ELECTRODE</u>:
- If the <u>metal</u> is <u>more reactive than hydrogen</u>, then <u>hydrogen</u> will be produced.
- If the <u>metal</u> is <u>less reactive than hydrogen</u>, then the <u>metal</u> will be produced.

<u>POSITIVE ELECTRODE</u>:
- <u>Oxygen</u> will be formed unless <u>halide ions</u> (Cl^-, Br^-, I^-) are present.
- If <u>halide</u> ions are present, then molecules of <u>chlorine</u>, <u>bromine</u> or <u>iodine</u> will be formed.

The Electrolysis of Sodium Chloride Solution

When an electric current is passed through sodium chloride solution <u>hydrogen</u>, <u>chlorine</u> and <u>sodium hydroxide</u> are formed.

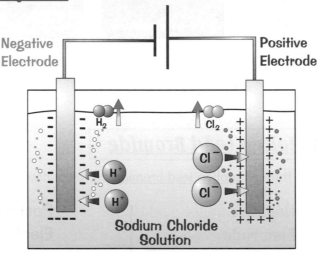

<u>Positive ions</u> move to the <u>negative electrode</u>. Here they <u>gain</u> <u>electrons</u> (reduction).

<u>Hydrogen</u> is produced.

<u>Negative ions</u> move to the <u>positive electrode</u>. Here they <u>lose</u> <u>electrons</u> (oxidation).

<u>Chlorine</u> is produced.

1) <u>Sodium</u> is not produced because it is <u>more reactive</u> than hydrogen. So sodium ions stay in the <u>solution</u>.

2) <u>Hydroxide ions</u> (from the water) join onto these sodium ions.

3) This means that <u>sodium hydroxide</u> is left in the solution.

Useful Products from the Electrolysis of Sodium Chloride Solution

The products of the electrolysis of sodium chloride solution have many uses in <u>industry</u>. For example:

- <u>Chlorine</u> is used to make <u>bleach</u> and <u>plastics</u>.
- <u>Sodium hydroxide</u> is used to make <u>soap</u>.

I use a positive iron — it keeps my clothes happy...

The trickiest bit on this page is probably <u>predicting the products</u> of electrolysis. Don't just whizz past it.

Extraction of Aluminium and Electroplating

I bet you never thought you'd <u>need to know so much</u> about electrolysis — but, sadly, <u>you do</u>.

Electrolysis is Used to Remove Aluminium from Aluminium Oxide

1) Aluminium's never found in the earth as a <u>pure metal</u>.
2) It can be removed from aluminium oxide using <u>electrolysis</u>.

Cryolite is Used to Lower the Temperature (and Costs)

1) <u>Aluminium oxide</u> has a very <u>high melting point</u> — so melting it for electrolysis would be very <u>expensive</u>.
2) <u>Instead</u> it is <u>dissolved</u> in <u>molten cryolite</u>.
3) This brings the <u>temperature down</u> which makes it <u>cheaper</u>.
4) <u>Aluminium</u> forms at the <u>negative electrode</u>. <u>Oxygen</u> forms at the <u>positive electrode</u>.
5) The <u>oxygen</u> then reacts with the <u>carbon</u> in the electrode to produce <u>carbon dioxide</u>.

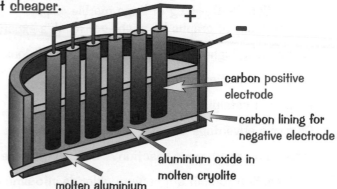

carbon positive electrode

carbon lining for negative electrode

aluminium oxide in molten cryolite

molten aluminium

Electroplating Uses Electrolysis

1) <u>Electroplating</u> uses electrolysis to <u>coat</u> the <u>surface of one metal</u> with <u>another metal</u>.
2) It has many <u>uses</u>:
   - <u>Decoration</u>: It's <u>cheaper</u> to plate a brass cup with silver, than to make the cup out of solid silver.
   - <u>Conduction</u>: Metals like <u>copper</u> conduct <u>electricity</u> well.
     So copper is often used to plate metals for <u>electronic circuits</u> and <u>computers</u>.

<u>Example</u>: To electroplate <u>silver</u> onto a <u>brass cup</u>:
1) Make the <u>brass cup</u> the negative electrode (to attract the positive silver ions).
2) Make a lump of <u>pure silver</u> the positive electrode.
3) Dip the electrodes in a solution of <u>silver ions</u> (e.g. silver nitrate).
4) The brass cup is <u>plated</u> with silver ions from the <u>solution</u>. The solution is <u>topped up</u> with silver ions from the <u>silver electrode</u>.

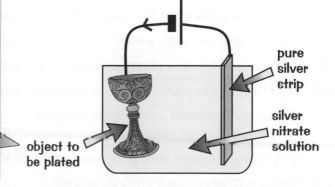

pure silver strip

silver nitrate solution

object to be plated

Silver electroplated text is worth a fortune...

Electroplating can be done with all sorts of metals. You just need to know about <u>silver</u> and <u>copper</u> plating.

Revision Summary for Chemistry 2b

Well here are some more of those nice questions that you enjoy so much.
If you can't answer any, go back to the page, do a bit more learning, then try again.

1) What are the four things that change the rate of a reaction?

2) Describe three different ways of measuring the rate of a reaction.

3)* A student does an experiment to find out how surface area affects the reaction between marble and hydrochloric acid. He measures the amount of gas given off at regular times.
He uses three samples for his experiment:
Sample A – 10 g of powdered marble
Sample B – 10 g of small marble chips
Sample C – 10 g of large marble chips
Sketch a set of graphs he might get for this experiment.

4) Explain why higher concentration makes collisions between particles happen more often.

5) What is activation energy?

6) What is a catalyst?

7) Give one advantage of using catalysts in industry. Then give one disadvantage.

8) What is an exothermic reaction? Give an example.

9) The reaction to split ammonium chloride into ammonia and hydrogen chloride is endothermic.
Will the reverse (backwards) reaction be exothermic or endothermic?

10) What does the pH scale show?

11) What type of ions are always present in a) acids and   b) alkalis?

12) Write down an equation to show what happens to the H^+ and OH^- ions in a neutralisation reaction.

13) Write down the state symbol that means 'dissolved in water'.

14) Acids react with some metals. What are the products?

15) Name a metal that doesn't react at all with dilute acids.

16) What type of salts are produced by:
a) hydrochloric acid?
b) sulfuric acid?

17) What type of reaction is "acid + metal oxide", or "acid + metal hydroxide"?

18) Suggest an acid and a metal oxide/hydroxide to mix to form the following salts.
a) copper chloride   b) magnesium nitrate   c) zinc sulfate

19) What is the product of the reaction between ammonia and nitric acid used for?

20) How can you tell when a neutralisation reaction is over if you're using an acid and an alkali?

21) How can precipitation reactions be used in the treatment of drinking water?

22) What happens to molten lead bromide when an electric current is passed through it?

23) a) Give one industrial use of sodium hydroxide.
b) Give two uses of chlorine.

24) Why is cryolite used during the electrolysis of aluminium oxide?

25) Give two different uses of electroplating.

* Answers on page 115

Chemistry 2b — Reaction Rates, Salts and Electrolysis

Velocity and Distance-Time Graphs

Ah, time for some lovely physics, you lucky thing. First off — <u>speed</u> and <u>velocity</u>.

Speed and Velocity are Both How Fast You're Going

1) <u>Speed and velocity</u> are both measured in <u>m/s</u> (or km/h or mph)
2) They both simply say <u>how fast</u> you're going.
3) But there's <u>one difference</u> between them which <u>you need to know</u>:

> <u>Speed</u> is just <u>how fast</u> you're going (e.g. 20 m/s) — the <u>direction doesn't matter</u>.
>
> <u>Velocity</u> is the speed in a given <u>direction</u>, e.g. 20 m/s north.

Distance-Time Graphs

1) A <u>distance-time graph</u> shows the <u>distance travelled</u> by an object over <u>time</u>.

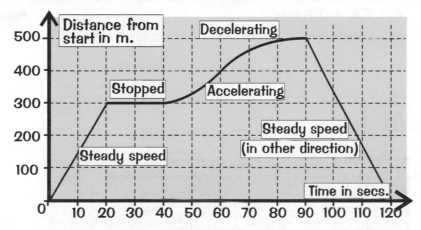

2) The <u>slope</u> of a distance-time graph is called the <u>gradient</u>.
3) The <u>gradient</u> of a distance-time graph tells you <u>how fast</u> your object is travelling.
4) <u>Flat</u> sections are where the object is <u>stationary</u> — it's <u>stopped</u>.
5) <u>Straight</u> uphill (/) or downhill (\) sections mean it is travelling at a <u>steady speed</u>.
6) The <u>steeper</u> the graph, the <u>faster</u> it's going.
7) <u>Downhill</u> sections mean it's <u>going back</u> towards its starting point.
8) <u>Curves</u> show a <u>change in speed</u>.
9) A <u>steepening</u> curve means it's <u>speeding up</u> (increasing gradient).
   This is called <u>acceleration</u> (see next page).
10) A <u>levelling off</u> curve means it's <u>slowing down</u> (decreasing gradient).
    This is called <u>deceleration</u> (see next page).

Curves = difficulty getting out of chairs.

I'm just like speed — I have no sense of direction...

Distance-time graphs have an annoying habit of popping up in exams <u>year after year</u> — so make sure you know how to <u>draw</u> and <u>understand</u> them. Remember that the <u>gradient</u> of a distance-time graph is the <u>speed</u> — so the <u>steeper</u> the line, the <u>faster</u> you're going. If you <u>really like</u> graphs, there's a special treat on the next page...

Acceleration and Velocity-Time Graphs

I bet you loved that distance-time graph, huh? Well here's its big brother — the <u>velocity-time</u> graph. Yikes.

Acceleration is How Quickly Velocity is Changing

Acceleration is <u>definitely not</u> the same as <u>velocity</u> or <u>speed</u>.

1) Acceleration is <u>how quickly</u> the velocity is <u>changing</u>.
2) This change in velocity can be a <u>CHANGE IN SPEED</u> or a <u>CHANGE IN DIRECTION</u> or <u>both</u>.

Acceleration — The Formula:

$$\text{Acceleration} = \frac{\text{Change in Velocity}}{\text{Time taken}} \qquad a = \frac{(v - u)}{t}$$

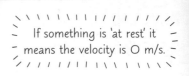

If something is 'at rest' it means the velocity is 0 m/s.

1) You need to work out the '<u>change in velocity</u>'.
2) Subtract the <u>initial</u> (starting) velocity, <u>u</u>, from the <u>final</u> velocity, <u>v</u>.

> <u>EXAMPLE:</u> A cat accelerates from 2 m/s to 6 m/s in 5.6 s. Find its acceleration.
>
> <u>ANSWER:</u> Using the formula: $a = (v - u) \div t = (6 - 2) \div 5.6$
> $= 4 \div 5.6 = \underline{0.71 \text{ m/s}^2}$
>
> Watch out for the units — acceleration is in m/s², <u>not</u> m/s.

Velocity-Time Graphs

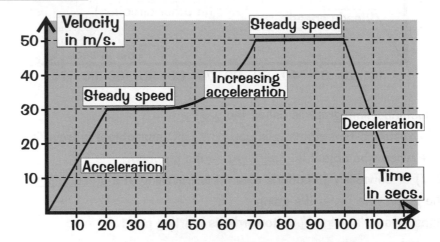

1) The <u>gradient</u> of a velocity-time graph tells you the <u>acceleration</u> of the object.
2) <u>Flat sections</u> shows the object is travelling at a <u>steady speed</u>.
3) <u>Uphill</u> sections (/) show <u>acceleration</u>.
4) <u>Downhill</u> sections (\\) show <u>deceleration</u>.
5) The <u>steeper</u> the graph, the <u>greater</u> the <u>acceleration</u> or <u>deceleration</u>.
6) A <u>curved</u> graph means the object has a <u>changing acceleration</u>.

Understanding motion graphs — it can be a real uphill struggle...

Make sure you know all there is to know about velocity-time graphs — i.e. <u>learn those numbered points</u>. Remember, the <u>gradient</u> of velocity-time graph is the <u>acceleration</u>. Right, that's enough graphs for now folks...

Weight, Mass and Gravity

Now for something a bit more attractive — the force of <u>gravity</u>. Enjoy...

Gravitational Force is the Force of Attraction Between All Masses

1) <u>Gravity</u> is a force that attracts (pulls) <u>all</u> masses.
2) But you only notice it when one of the masses is <u>really really big</u>, e.g. a planet.
3) Anything near a planet or star is <u>attracted</u> to it <u>very strongly</u>.
4) You need to know these <u>three</u> important things about <u>gravity</u>:

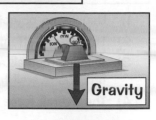

- On the surface of a planet, it makes all things <u>accelerate</u> (see p. 72) towards the <u>ground</u>.
- Objects all fall with the <u>same</u> acceleration, g, which is about <u>10 m/s^2</u> on Earth.
- It gives everything a <u>weight</u>.

Weight and Mass are Not the Same

1) <u>Mass</u> is just the <u>amount of 'stuff'</u> in an object. The mass of an object <u>never changes</u> — no matter where it is in the universe.
2) <u>Weight</u> is caused by the <u>pull</u> of the <u>gravitational force</u>.
3) An object has the <u>same</u> mass whether it's on <u>Earth</u> or on the <u>Moon</u> — but its <u>weight</u> will be <u>different</u>.
4) A 1 kg mass will <u>weigh less</u> on the Moon (about 1.6 N) than it does on Earth (about 10 N), because the <u>gravitational force</u> pulling on it is <u>less</u>.
5) Weight is a <u>force</u> measured in <u>newtons</u>. Mass is <u>not</u> a force.

The Very Important Formula for Mass, Weight and Gravity

weight = mass × gravitational field strength

$$W = m \times g$$

1) "g" is the <u>strength</u> of gravity. Its value is <u>different</u> for <u>different planets</u>.
2) <u>On Earth</u> g is about 10 N/kg. <u>On the Moon</u>, where the gravity is weaker, g is only about 1.6 N/kg.

Example: What is the weight, in newtons, of a 5 kg mass:
            a) on Earth?   b) on the Moon?

Answers: "W = m × g". a) On Earth: Weight = 5 × 10 = <u>50 N</u>
                          b) On the Moon: Weight = 5 × 1.6 = <u>8 N</u>

Resultant Forces

Gravity isn't the only force in town — there are other forces that you need to know about too.

Resultant Force is the Overall Force on an Object

1) Usually an object will have <u>lots</u> of <u>forces</u> acting on it.

2) The <u>overall</u> effect of these forces will decide the <u>motion</u> of the object (how it will move).

3) If the forces all act in a <u>straight line</u> in the <u>same</u> or the <u>opposite</u> direction, you can find the <u>overall force</u> on the object by just <u>adding or subtracting</u> them.

4) The overall force you get is called the <u>resultant force</u>.

Example: Stationary Teapot — All Forces Balance

1) The force of <u>GRAVITY</u> (or weight) is acting <u>downwards</u> on the teapot (see p. 73).

2) This causes a <u>REACTION FORCE</u> from the table's surface <u>pushing up</u> on the teapot.

3) The <u>reaction force</u> and <u>weight</u> are <u>equal</u> and <u>opposite</u>. They cancel each other out — the <u>resultant force</u> is <u>zero</u>.

4) This means the <u>forces</u> on the teapot are in <u>BALANCE</u> (it isn't moving — it's velocity stays at zero).

5) <u>Without</u> a reaction force, it would <u>accelerate</u> <u>downwards</u> due to the pull of gravity.

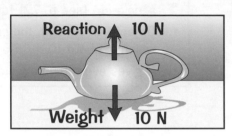

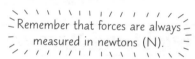

Remember that forces are always measured in newtons (N).

A Resultant Force Means a Change in Velocity

1) If there is a <u>resultant force</u> acting on an object, then the object's <u>motion</u> will <u>change</u>.

2) In other words it causes a <u>change in the object's velocity</u>, or causes it to <u>move</u> if it was <u>stationary</u>.

<u>EXAMPLE:</u> Benny is driving to Las Vegas in his sports car. The car has a driving force of <u>1000 N</u>. <u>600 N</u> of air resistance also acts on the car in the opposite direction.
 a) What is the <u>resultant force</u> on the car?
 b) Will the car's velocity <u>change</u>?

<u>ANSWER:</u> a) Say that the forces pointing to the <u>left</u> are pointing in the <u>positive direction</u>. (So forces pointing to the <u>right</u> are pointing in the <u>negative direction</u>.)

Add the forces together to find the resultant force:

1000 N + (−600 N) = 1000 − 600 = <u>400 N</u> to the left.

Driving Force: 1000 N

Air Resistance: 600 N

Resultant Force: 400 N

 b) There is a resultant force, so Benny's velocity <u>will</u> change. Viva Las Vegas.

And you're moving forward — what a result...

Resultant forces are just about <u>adding</u> and <u>subtracting</u> forces that are acting in the <u>same</u> or <u>opposite</u> directions. Next up, some of the <u>thrilling physics</u> you can understand once you have resultant forces figured out.

Forces and Acceleration

Need a little push to get you going with your revision? You need a <u>resultant force</u>...

An Object Needs a Force to Start Moving

If the resultant force on a <u>stationary</u> object is <u>zero</u>, the object will <u>remain stationary</u>.

Things <u>don't just start moving</u> on their own, there has to be a <u>resultant force</u> (see p. 74) to get them started.

No Resultant Force Means No Change in Velocity

If there is <u>no resultant force</u> on a <u>moving</u> object it'll just carry on moving at the <u>same velocity</u>.

1) When a train or car or bus or anything else is <u>moving</u> at a <u>constant velocity</u> then the <u>forces</u> on it must all be <u>balanced</u>.

2) You <u>DON'T</u> need a constant overall force to <u>keep</u> an object moving.

3) To keep going at a <u>steady speed</u>, there must be <u>zero resultant force</u> — don't you forget that folks.

A Resultant Force Means Acceleration

If the <u>resultant force</u> is <u>not zero</u>, then the object will <u>accelerate</u> in the direction of the force.

1) A <u>resultant</u> force that isn't zero will always produce <u>acceleration</u> (or deceleration).

2) This "<u>acceleration</u>" can take <u>five</u> different forms: <u>Starting</u>, <u>stopping</u>, <u>speeding up</u>, <u>slowing down</u> and <u>changing direction</u>.

3) On a force diagram, the <u>arrows</u> will be <u>unequal</u>:

<u>Don't ever say</u>: "If something's moving there must be an overall resultant force acting on it". Not so. If there's an <u>overall</u> force it will always <u>accelerate</u>. You get <u>steady</u> speed when there is <u>zero</u> resultant force.

Want to travel at a steady speed? Just say no to resultant forces...

This is tricky stuff. Just remember, if an object <u>isn't moving</u> or is moving at a <u>steady speed</u> it means that there is <u>zero resultant force</u> acting on. A <u>resultant force</u> that isn't zero will produce an acceleration. My brain hurts.

Forces and Acceleration

More fun stuff on <u>resultant forces</u> and <u>acceleration</u> here. Oh happy day.

A Non-Zero Resultant Force Produces an Acceleration

Any <u>resultant force</u> will produce <u>acceleration</u>, and this is the <u>formula</u> for it:

$$F = ma \qquad or \qquad a = F/m$$

m = mass in kilograms (kg)
a = acceleration in metres per second squared (m/s²)
F is the <u>resultant force</u> in newtons (N)

<u>EXAMPLE:</u> A car of mass of 1750 kg has an engine which provides a driving force of 5200 N. Find its acceleration when first setting off from rest.

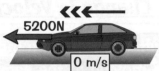

5200N

0 m/s

If something starts from rest, its starting velocity is zero.

<u>ANSWER:</u> Resultant force = 5200 N
a = F/m = 5200 ÷ 1750 = <u>3.0 m/s²</u>

Reaction Forces are Equal and Opposite

When <u>two objects interact</u>, the forces they exert on each other are <u>equal and opposite</u>.

1) That means if you <u>push</u> something, say a trolley, the trolley will <u>push back</u> against you, <u>just as hard</u>.

2) And as soon as you <u>stop</u> pushing, <u>so does the trolley</u>. Clever.

3) The tricky thing to understand is — if the forces are always equal, <u>how does anything ever go anywhere</u>?

4) The important thing to remember is that the two forces are acting on <u>different objects</u>.

5) Think about a pair of ice skaters:

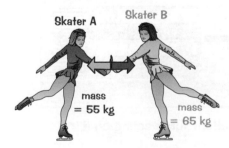

Skater A
Skater B
mass = 55 kg
mass = 65 kg

- When skater A pushes on skater B (the '<u>action</u>' force), she feels an equal and opposite force from skater B's hand (the '<u>reaction</u>' force).

- Both skaters feel the <u>same sized force</u>, in <u>opposite directions</u>, and so accelerate away from each other.

- <u>a = F/m</u>, so skater A will be <u>accelerated</u> more than skater B, because she has a smaller mass.

I have a reaction to forces — they bring me out in a rash...

This is the real deal. Like... proper Physics. It was <u>pretty fantastic</u> at the time it was discovered — suddenly people understood what made things move. Interesting, hey? No? Shame. Sadly, you've got to learn it anyway.

Frictional Force and Drag

Ever wondered why it's so hard to run into the wind whilst wearing a sandwich board? Read on to find out...

Friction is Always There to Slow Things Down

1) Friction is a force that always acts in the <u>opposite</u> direction to movement.
2) You get friction when <u>two surfaces</u> rub together, or when an object passes <u>through a fluid</u>.
3) If an object has <u>no force</u> driving it along it will always <u>slow down and stop</u>.
4) This is because of <u>friction</u> with the air (unless you're in space where there's nothing to rub against).
5) To travel at a <u>steady</u> speed, the driving force needs to <u>balance</u> the frictional forces.

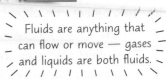
Fluids are anything that can flow or move — gases and liquids are both fluids.

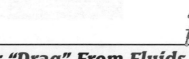

Resistance or "Drag" From Fluids

1) Most of the resistive (frictional) forces on a moving object are caused by <u>air resistance</u> or "<u>drag</u>".

2) The <u>shape</u> of an object affects the <u>drag</u> on it as it <u>moves</u> through a <u>fluid</u>.
3) Shapes that only cause a small amount of drag are <u>aerodynamic</u> (<u>streamlined</u>).
4) Some things are <u>designed</u> to be aerodynamic. E.g. a <u>sports car</u> (see p.84) or an <u>aeroplane</u>.

5) <u>Parachutes</u> are designed to have a <u>large</u> amount of <u>air resistance</u> (see next page).

Frictional Force Increases as the Speed Increases

1) <u>Frictional forces</u> from fluids always <u>increase with speed</u>.
2) A car has <u>much more</u> friction to <u>work against</u> when travelling at <u>70 mph</u> compared to <u>30 mph</u>.
3) So at 70 mph the engine has to work <u>much harder</u> just to maintain a <u>steady speed</u>.

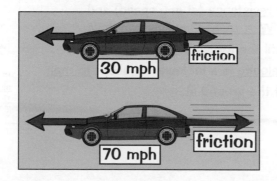

Learning about air resistance — it can be a real drag...

There are a couple of really important things on this page. 1) When you fall through a fluid, there's a frictional force (drag). 2) The faster you fall, the greater the frictional force that acts on you. Got that? Lovely.

Terminal Velocity

This page is all about stuff <u>falling</u> from above. Don't be scared... but wear a <u>helmet</u> if it makes you feel better.

Objects Falling Through Fluids Reach a Terminal Velocity

1) When a falling object first <u>sets off</u>, the force of <u>gravity</u> pulling it down is <u>greater</u> than the <u>air resistance</u> slowing it down.

2) This means the object <u>accelerates</u>.

3) As the <u>speed increases</u>, the air resistance <u>builds up</u>.

4) This slowly <u>reduces</u> the <u>acceleration</u>.

5) Eventually the <u>air resistance</u> is <u>equal</u> to the <u>accelerating force</u> and then the object won't accelerate any more. The <u>resultant force</u> is <u>zero</u>.

6) It will have reached its maximum speed or <u>terminal velocity</u> and will fall at a steady speed.

See page 72 for more on velocity-time graphs.

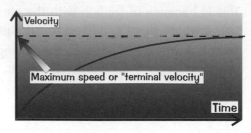

The Terminal Velocity of Falling Objects Depends on Shape and Area

1) The <u>accelerating force</u> acting on <u>all</u> falling objects is <u>gravity</u> (see p.73).

2) If there was <u>no air resistance</u>, <u>gravity</u> would make all falling objects fall with the <u>same</u> acceleration.

3) On the Moon, there's <u>no air</u>, so hammers and feathers dropped at the same time will hit the ground <u>together</u>.

4) But, on Earth, <u>air resistance</u> causes things to fall at <u>different</u> speeds.

5) The air resistance acting on an object depends on its <u>shape and area</u> (see p.77).

6) The <u>terminal velocity</u> of any object depends on its <u>air resistance</u> compared to its <u>weight</u>.

Example: Human Skydiver

1) A <u>skydiver</u> jumps out of a plane.

2) Without his parachute open he has quite a <u>small area</u>.

3) He has a force of "$W = m \times g$" pulling him down (see p.73).

4) He reaches a <u>terminal velocity</u> of about <u>120 mph</u>.

5) But with the parachute <u>open</u>, he has a <u>larger surface area</u>.

6) So there's much more <u>air resistance</u> (at any speed) and still only the same force "$W = m \times g$" pulling him down.

7) His velocity <u>decreases</u> until the forces become <u>equal</u> again.

8) This means his <u>terminal velocity</u> is a lot lower — about <u>15 mph</u>.

9) This is a <u>safe speed</u> to hit the ground at.

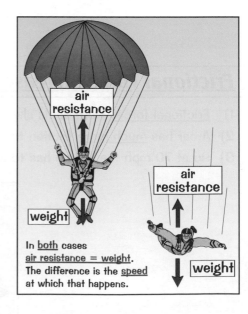

Oh terminal velocity — I've really fallen for you...

Skydiving and terminal velocity — this is physics at its most <u>extreme</u>. Make sure you know why a parachute <u>reduces</u> the terminal velocity of a skydiver — it's all do with there being <u>more air resistance</u>. Party on dudes.

Stopping Distances

And now a page on stopping distances. This kind of physics really drives me crazy.

Many Things Affect Your Total Stopping Distance

1) The _faster_ a vehicle's going, the _bigger braking force_ you'll need _to stop_ it in a _certain distance_.

2) For a certain braking force, the _faster_ you're going, the _greater your stopping distance_.

3) The total _stopping distance_ of a vehicle is the distance covered in the time between the driver _first spotting_ a hazard (danger) and the vehicle _stopping_.

4) The _stopping distance_ is _the total_ of the _thinking distance_ and the _braking distance_.

1) Thinking Distance

"The distance the vehicle travels during the driver's reaction time".

~ The reaction time is the time between the driver spotting a hazard and hitting the brakes. ~

It's affected by _two main factors_:

a) **How fast you're going** — The _faster_ you're going, the _further_ you'll go.

b) **How dopey you are** — _Tiredness_, _drugs_ and _alcohol_ can _increase_ the _time_ it takes you to _react_.

Distractions (e.g. messing about with the radio, heavy rain), may mean a driver _doesn't notice_ a hazard until they're quite _close_ to it.

This _doesn't_ affect your thinking distance, but you _start thinking_ about stopping when you are _nearer_ to the hazard — so you're _more likely_ to crash.

The figures below for stopping distances are from the Highway Code. It's frightening to see just how far it takes to stop when you're going at 70 mph.

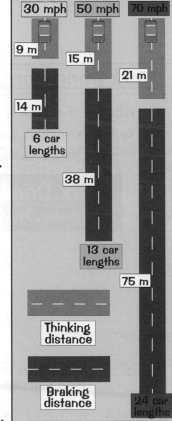

2) Braking Distance

"The distance the car travels under the braking force (i.e. while braking)".

It's affected by _four main factors_:

a) **How fast you're going** — The _faster_ you're going, the _further_ it takes to stop.

b) **How good your brakes are** — Worn out or faulty brakes will let you down just when you need them the _most_, i.e. in an _emergency_.

c) **How good the tyres are** — _Tyres_ need to be in _good condition_ so they can _grip_ in _wet_ conditions.

d) **How good the grip is** — This depends on _three things_:
   1) _road surface_, 2) _weather_ conditions, 3) _tyres_.

Wet or _icy roads_ are always much more _slippy_ than dry roads.
You don't have as much grip when you _brake_, so you travel further before stopping.

Stop right there — and learn this page...

Woah, lots of stuff to learn from this page. Make sure you know what _thinking_ and _braking_ distance are. Learn all the _factors_ that affect them too. For example, _tiredness_ can increase thinking distance. (And _decrease_ revision.)

Work Done

Don't be fooled by the title of this page. Our work is <u>not done</u> yet. There's <u>more</u> stuff to learn. Boo. Hiss.

Work is Done When a Force Moves an Object Through a Distance

> When a <u>force</u> moves an <u>object</u> through a <u>distance</u>,
> <u>ENERGY IS TRANSFERRED</u> and <u>WORK IS DONE</u>.

That sounds confusing. Try this:

1) Whenever something <u>moves</u>, something else is supplying some sort of '<u>effort</u>' to move it.

2) The thing putting the <u>effort</u> in needs a <u>supply</u> of <u>energy</u> (like <u>fuel</u> or <u>food</u> or <u>electricity</u> etc.).

3) It then does '<u>work</u>' by <u>moving</u> the object — and it <u>transfers</u> the energy it receives (as fuel) into <u>other forms</u>.

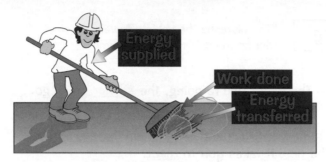

4) Whether this energy is transferred '<u>usefully</u>' or is '<u>wasted</u>' — you can still say that '<u>work is done</u>'.

5) '<u>Work done</u>' and '<u>energy transferred</u>' are the <u>same thing</u>. (And they're both measured in <u>joules</u>.)

Work Done, Force and Distance are Linked by an Equation

1) Whether the force is <u>friction</u> or <u>weight</u> or <u>tension in a rope</u>, it's always the same.

2) To find how much <u>energy</u> has been <u>transferred</u> (in joules), you just multiply the <u>force in N</u> by the <u>distance moved in m</u>.

> **Work Done = Force × Distance**
> (joules, J)   (newtons, N)   (metres, m)
>
> **W = F × d**

<u>EXAMPLE:</u> Some yobs drag an old tractor tyre <u>5 m</u> over rough ground.
They pull with a total force of <u>340 N</u>. Find the energy transferred.

<u>ANSWER:</u> W = F×d = 340 × 5 = <u>1700 J</u>.

<u>Revise work done — what else...</u>

So "<u>energy transferred</u>" and "<u>work done</u>" are the same thing. Remember, that work is done when a <u>force</u> moves an object through a <u>distance</u>. I like to practise doing work by lifting a <u>fig roll</u> from the <u>packet</u> to my <u>mouth</u>.

Kinetic and Potential Energy

As a song once said "You raise me up... so I can gain gravitational potential energy." Or something like that.

Gravitational Potential Energy is Energy Due to Height

1) Gravitational potential energy is the energy that an object has because of its height in a gravitational field.

2) A gravitational field is just a fancy way of saying somewhere where gravity acts on objects.

3) When an object is lifted vertically (straight up), work is done against the force of gravity (it takes effort to lift it up). The object gains gravitational potential energy.

4) You can work out how much gravitational potential energy an object gains using this formula:

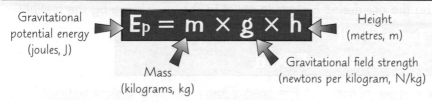

Gravitational Potential Energy = mass × g × height

$$E_p = m \times g \times h$$

Gravitational potential energy (joules, J)

Mass (kilograms, kg)

Gravitational field strength (newtons per kilogram, N/kg)

Height (metres, m)

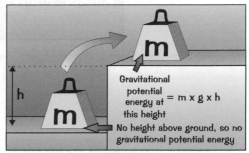

Gravitational potential energy at this height $= m \times g \times h$

No height above ground, so no gravitational potential energy

5) On Earth the gravitational field strength (g) is about 10 N/kg.

EXAMPLE: A sheep of mass 47 kg is slowly raised through 6.3 m. Find the gain in gravitational potential energy.

ANSWER: Just plug the numbers into the formula:
$E_p = m \times g \times h = 47 \times 10 \times 6.3 = \underline{2961\ J}$ (Joules because it's energy.)

Kinetic Energy is Energy of Movement

1) Anything that's moving has kinetic energy.

2) There's a crazy looking formula for it:

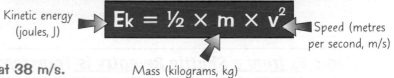

Kinetic Energy = ½ × mass × speed^2

$$E_k = \tfrac{1}{2} \times m \times v^2$$

Kinetic energy (joules, J)

Speed (metres per second, m/s)

Mass (kilograms, kg)

EXAMPLE: A car of mass 2450 kg is travelling at 38 m/s. Calculate its kinetic energy.

ANSWER: Plug the numbers into the formula — but watch the 'v²'!
$E_k = \tfrac{1}{2} \times m \times v^2 = \tfrac{1}{2} \times 2450 \times 38^2 = \underline{1\ 768\ 900\ J}$ (Joules because it's energy.)

3) Remember, the kinetic energy of something depends both on mass and speed.

4) The heavier it is and the faster it's going, the bigger its kinetic energy will be.

small mass, not fast low kinetic energy

big fast lorries Ltd

big mass, real fast high kinetic energy

Kinetic energy — it really moves me...

Eek. Don't let those two formulas scare you. You've just got to practise putting the numbers into them. Cover up the answers to the two examples above, and have a go at answering them yourself. Then have a biscuit as a reward.

Work and Kinetic Energy

When <u>work</u> is done, <u>energy</u> is <u>transferred</u>. This page is all about <u>kinetic energy</u> being transferred into <u>other</u> types of energy when <u>work is done</u>. Sounds confusing? Read on...

Kinetic Energy Transferred is Work Done

When a Car is Moving It Has Kinetic Energy

1) A <u>moving car</u> can have a lot of <u>kinetic energy</u>.

2) To stop or slow down a car this kinetic energy needs to be <u>transferred into other types of energy</u>.

3) When the <u>brakes</u> are used, work is done by the <u>friction</u> between the <u>wheels</u> and the <u>brake pads</u>.

4) This transfers the <u>kinetic energy</u> into <u>heat energy</u> and causes the <u>temperature</u> of the brakes to <u>increase</u>.

5) The <u>kinetic energy</u> transferred by the car during <u>braking</u> is equal to the <u>work done</u> by the <u>brakes</u>:

> Kinetic Energy Transferred = Work Done by Brakes
> $$\tfrac{1}{2} \times m \times v^2 = F \times d$$

m = <u>mass</u> of car and passengers (in kg)   v = <u>speed</u> of car (in m/s)   F = <u>braking force</u> (in N)   d = <u>braking distance</u> (in m).

Falling Objects Convert E_p into E_k

1) When something falls, its <u>gravitational potential energy</u> (E_P) is <u>converted</u> into <u>kinetic energy</u> (E_K).

2) So the <u>further</u> it falls, the <u>faster</u> it goes.

3) We can usually <u>ignore air resistance</u> when talking about falling objects.

4) This means we can say that for a <u>falling object</u>:

> Kinetic energy <u>gained</u> = Gravitational potential energy <u>lost</u>

Some E_k from a Shuttle Re-entry is Transferred into Heat and Sound

1) When <u>meteors</u> and <u>space shuttles</u> enter the atmosphere, they have a <u>very high kinetic energy</u>.

2) <u>Friction</u> between the object and the atmosphere (see p.77) transfers some of their kinetic energy to <u>heat energy</u> and <u>work is done</u>.

3) <u>Most</u> meteors get so hot that they <u>burn up</u> completely and never hit the Earth.

4) Only the biggest meteors make it through to the Earth's surface — these are called <u>meteorites</u>.

5) Space shuttles have heat shields made from <u>special materials</u> which lose heat <u>quickly</u>.

6) This allows the shuttle to re-enter the atmosphere <u>without burning up</u>.

<u>Kinetic energy — just get a move on and learn it, OK...</u>

So <u>that's</u> why I've not been hit by a meteor — most get burned up. Now you know. Remember, when energy is <u>transferred</u> from one type to another, <u>work is done</u>. For example, work is done by the brakes to stop a car — they <u>transfer</u> the kinetic energy of the car to heat energy and so the <u>temperature</u> of the brakes increases.

Forces and Elasticity

Forces aren't just important for cars and falling sheep — you can <u>stretch things</u> with them as well.

Work Done to an Elastic Object is Stored as Elastic Potential Energy

1) Forces can be used to <u>stretch</u> and <u>change the shape</u> of objects.
2) Any object that can <u>go back</u> to its <u>original shape</u> after the force has been taken away is an <u>elastic object</u>.
3) <u>Work</u> has to be done to an elastic object to <u>change</u> its shape.
4) When this happens, energy is <u>stored</u> by the object as <u>elastic potential energy</u>.
5) The elastic potential energy is then <u>converted to</u> <u>kinetic energy</u> when the <u>force is removed</u>...
6) ...and the object returns to its <u>original</u> shape, e.g. when a spring or an elastic band bounces back.

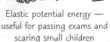

Elastic potential energy —
useful for passing exams and
scaring small children

Extension of an Elastic Object is Directly Proportional to Force

1) If a spring is held at the top and then a weight attached to the bottom, it <u>stretches</u>.

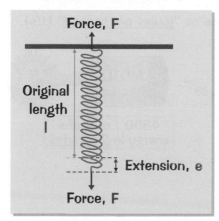

Force, F

Original length l

Extension, e

Force, F

2) As you add <u>more</u> weights to a spring, it will <u>extend</u> (stretch) <u>more</u>.
3) The <u>force</u> and the <u>extension</u> are <u>directly proportional</u>.
4) This is just a fancy way of saying the force is the extension <u>multiplied</u> by a <u>constant</u> number.
5) This constant is called the <u>spring constant</u>, <u>k</u>.
6) k depends on the <u>material</u> that you are stretching.
7) This is the equation you need to learn:

Force (newtons, N)

$$F = k \times e$$

Extension (metres, m)

Spring constant (newtons per metre, N/m)

<u>EXAMPLE</u>: A mass hung from the end of a spring makes it extend by 0.25 m. The spring constant, k, for the spring is 20 N/m. Work out the force on the spring.

<u>ANSWER</u>: $F = k \times e = 20 \times 0.25 = \underline{5\ N}$. Ta da.

Stretch an Elastic Object Too Much and it Won't go Back to its Original Shape

1) There is a <u>maximum</u> force that the elastic object can take and still extend proportionally.
2) This is known as the <u>limit of proportionality</u>.
3) If you increase the force <u>past</u> the limit of proportionality, the material will be <u>permanently stretched</u> (it won't go back to its original shape).
4) This means that when the force is <u>removed</u>, the material will be <u>longer</u> than at the start.

I could make a joke, but I don't want to stretch myself...

Scaring small children aside, elastic potential is really <u>quite a useful</u> form of energy. Think of all the things we rely on that use it — catapults, trampolines... Ah, elastic potential energy — thank you for making our lives better.

Power

You hear the word power said a lot. In physics, power means the <u>rate</u> that <u>energy</u> is <u>transferred</u>. Ooooh.

Power is the "Rate of Doing Work" — i.e. How Much per Second

1) <u>Power</u> is <u>not</u> the same thing as <u>force</u>, nor <u>energy</u>.
2) A <u>powerful</u> machine is not necessarily one which can exert a strong <u>force</u> (though they usually can).
3) A <u>powerful</u> machine is one which transfers <u>a lot of energy in a short space of time</u>.
4) The energy transferred can be <u>any type</u> of energy, e.g. potential energy or kinetic energy.
5) This is the <u>formula</u> for power:

$$\text{Power} = \frac{\text{Work done (or energy transferred)}}{\text{Time taken}}$$

$$P = \frac{E}{t}$$

Power is Measured in Watts (or J/s)

1) The proper unit of power is the <u>watt</u>.
2) <u>One watt = 1 joule of energy transferred per second.</u>
3) <u>Power</u> means "how much energy <u>per second</u>", so <u>watts</u> are the same as "<u>joules per second</u>" (J/s).

Example: A motor transfers 4800 J of useful energy in 2 minutes. Find its power output.

Answer: First, convert 2 minutes into seconds:
2 × 60 = 120 seconds
So, P = E ÷ t = 4800 ÷ 120 = 40 W (or 40 J/s)

4800 J of useful
energy in <u>2 minutes</u>

Cars Have Different Power Ratings

1) The <u>power</u> of a <u>car engine</u> depends on the engine's <u>size</u> and <u>design</u>.
2) The <u>more powerful</u> an engine is, the more <u>energy</u> it transfers from its <u>fuel</u> every second and so the <u>faster</u> its top speed can be.

Small car
power output
= 50 kW

Sports car
power output
= 100 kW

3) Cars are also designed to be <u>aerodynamic</u>.
4) This means that they are shaped so that <u>air flows</u> very easily and smoothly past them.
5) This reduces the <u>air resistance</u> on them (see page 77).
6) A car reaches its <u>top speed</u> when the <u>driving forces</u> and <u>resistive forces</u> (e.g. air resistance) are <u>equal</u>.
7) Aerodynamic cars usually have a <u>higher top speed</u> as they will reach a higher speed <u>before</u> this happens.

Power — you need to know watt's watt...

Power is the amount of energy transferred per second, and it's measured in <u>watts</u>. Make sure you know <u>how</u> the <u>top speed</u> of a car can be <u>increased</u> by changing its <u>shape</u> and <u>power</u>. Ah physics, it truly is life in the <u>fast lane</u>.

Momentum and Collisions

A <u>large</u> rhino running very <u>fast</u> at you is going to be a lot harder to stop than a scrawny one out for a Sunday afternoon stroll — that's momentum for you.

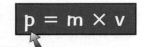

Momentum = Mass × Velocity

1) All <u>moving objects</u> have <u>momentum</u>.

2) The <u>greater</u> the <u>mass</u> of an object and the <u>greater</u> its <u>velocity</u>, the <u>more momentum</u> the object has.

3) Momentum is a <u>vector</u> quantity — it has size <u>and</u> direction.

4) You can work out the momentum of an object using this <u>formula</u>:

$$\text{Momentum (kg m/s)} = \text{Mass (kg)} \times \text{Velocity (m/s)} \qquad p = m \times v$$

This p stands for momentum... confusing, huh?

Momentum Before = Momentum After

1) In collisions and explosions, <u>momentum</u> is <u>conserved</u>.

2) This means the total momentum <u>before</u> is the same as <u>after</u>. This is called <u>Conservation of Momentum</u>.

<u>EXAMPLE</u>: Two skaters skate towards each other. They collide and move off together as shown. Find their total momentum after the collision.

<u>ANSWER</u>:

1) Choose which direction is <u>positive</u>. I'll say "<u>positive</u>" means "<u>to the right</u>".

2) <u>Total momentum before</u> collision
= momentum of Ed + momentum of Sue
= {80 × 2} + {60 × (–1.5)}
= <u>70 kg m/s</u>

<u>Total momentum after</u> collision
= <u>total momentum before</u> collision
= <u>70 kg m/s</u>

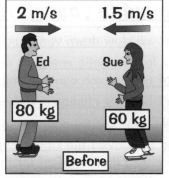

2 m/s   1.5 m/s   Final Velocity

Ed   Sue

80 kg   60 kg   (80+60) kg

Before   After

Forces Cause Changes in Momentum

1) When a <u>force</u> acts on an object, it causes a <u>change</u> in momentum.

2) A <u>larger</u> force means a <u>faster</u> change of momentum (and so a greater <u>acceleration</u> — see p.72).

3) Likewise, if someone's momentum changes <u>very quickly</u> (like in a <u>car crash</u>), the <u>forces</u> on the body will be very <u>large</u>, and more likely to cause <u>injury</u>.

4) Cars are designed with safety features (p.86) to slow people down over a <u>longer time</u> when they have a crash.

5) The longer it takes for people to change <u>momentum</u>, the <u>smaller</u> the <u>force</u> on them will be.

Learn this stuff — it'll only take a moment... um...

Remember, momentum is <u>conserved</u> in collisions and explosions. That means that the total momentum <u>before</u>, is the same as the total momentum <u>after</u>. Which makes questions like the one above a bit easier to work out. Yay.

Car Design and Safety

A lot of the physics from this section can be used in the real world to design safe and less wasteful cars...

Brakes do Work Against the Kinetic Energy of the Car

1) When you use the brakes to slow down a car, work is done (see p.80).
2) The brakes reduce the kinetic energy of the car by transferring it into heat (and sound) energy (see p.82).
3) In traditional braking systems that would be the end of the story...
4) ...but new regenerative braking systems used in some cars store the energy, instead of transferring it all into heat:

1) Regenerative brakes put the vehicle's motor into reverse — instead of converting the vehicle's kinetic energy into heat energy. This slows down the wheels.
2) At the same time, the motor acts as an electric generator.
3) The motor converts kinetic energy into electrical energy.
4) This is stored as chemical energy in the vehicle's battery.
5) So regenerative brakes store the energy transferred by braking rather than wasting it.

Cars are Designed to Convert Kinetic Energy Safely in a Crash

1) If a car crashes it will slow down very quickly.
2) This means that a lot of kinetic energy is converted into other forms of energy in a short amount of time, which can be dangerous for the people inside.
3) In a crash, there'll be a big change in momentum (see p.85) over a very short time.
4) So the people inside the car experience huge forces that could be fatal.
5) Cars are designed to convert the kinetic energy of the car and its passengers in a way that is safest for the passengers.
6) They often do this by increasing the time over which momentum changes happen, which reduces the forces on the passengers.
7) Here are some safety features found in cars, and how they reduce the forces in a crash:

air bag

seat belt

Feature	Details
Crumple Zones	1) Crumple zones at the front and back of the car crumple (squash) up on impact. 2) The car's kinetic energy is converted into other forms of energy by the car body as it changes shape. 3) Crumple zones increase the impact time, decreasing the force produced by the change in momentum.
Side impact bars	1) Side impact bars are strong metal tubes fitted into car door panels. 2) They help direct the kinetic energy of the crash away from the passengers to other areas of the car, e.g. crumple zones.
Seat belts	1) Seat belts stretch slightly, increasing the time taken for the wearer to stop. 2) This reduces the forces acting in the chest. 3) Some of the kinetic energy of the wearer is absorbed by the seat belt stretching.
Air bags	1) They slow you down more slowly so that the change in momentum happens over a longer time. 2) This reduces the forces acting on the passengers. 3) They also stop you from hitting hard surfaces inside the car.

Don't let all this revising drive you crazy...

Driving can be quite risky when you look at the physics of it — that's why lots of effort is put into making cars safe.

Static Electricity

Static electricity is all about <u>charges</u> that <u>can't</u> move. This means they <u>build up</u> in one place, and you often end up with a <u>spark</u> or a <u>shock</u> when they finally do move.

Static Electricity can Build Up when Materials are Rubbed Together

1) <u>Insulating materials</u> are materials that electrical charges <u>can't</u> move through easily.

2) When certain <u>insulating</u> materials are <u>rubbed</u> together, they become <u>electrically charged</u>.

3) <u>Negatively</u> charged particles called <u>electrons</u> are <u>scraped off one</u> material and <u>dumped</u> on the other.

4) The material that <u>gains electrons</u> becomes <u>negatively</u> charged.

5) The material that <u>loses electrons</u> is left with an <u>equal</u> but <u>positive</u> charge.

6) It is only ever the <u>electrons</u> that move — <u>not</u> the atoms.

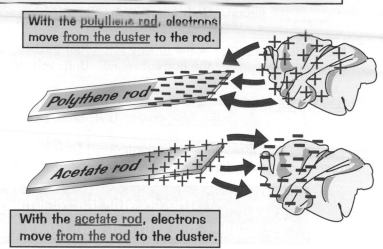

With the <u>polythene rod</u>, electrons move <u>from the duster</u> to the rod.

Polythene rod

Acetate rod

With the <u>acetate rod</u>, electrons move <u>from the rod</u> to the duster.

Like Charges Repel, Opposite Charges Attract

1) When two <u>charged objects</u> are brought close together they each <u>feel a force</u> from the other.

2) Two things with <u>opposite</u> electric charges are <u>attracted</u> to each other.

3) Two things with the <u>same</u> electric charge will <u>repel</u> each other.

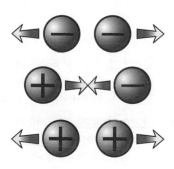

Electrical Charges can Move Easily Through Metals

1) Electrical charges can <u>move easily</u> through some materials.

2) These materials are called <u>conductors</u>.

3) <u>Metals</u> are known to be <u>good</u> conductors.

Electrons always put me in a bad mood — they're so negative...

The basic electrical charge carrier is the <u>electron</u>. They get just about everywhere in metals, taking <u>charge</u> pretty much wherever you want it. But in insulators they're <u>stuck</u> and can't move easily. Its only when materials are <u>rubbed together</u> that they ever get to go anywhere, poor lambs...

Current and Potential Difference

Isn't <u>electricity</u> great. Mind you it's pretty bad news if the <u>words</u> don't mean anything to you...
Hey, I know — learn them now!

1) <u>Current</u> is the <u>flow</u> of electric charge round the circuit. Unit: ampere, A.

2) <u>Potential Difference</u> is the <u>driving force</u> that pushes the current round. Unit: volt, V.

3) <u>Resistance</u> is anything in the circuit which <u>slows the flow down</u>. Unit: ohm, Ω.

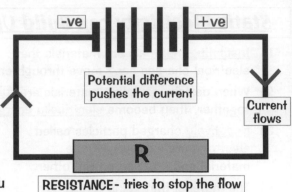

Potential difference pushes the current

Current flows

RESISTANCE- tries to stop the flow

The <u>current</u> that flows through a <u>component</u> (any item in the you can put in a circuit) depends on the <u>resistance</u> of the component:

> The <u>greater the resistance</u> of a component,
> the <u>smaller the current</u> that flows (for a given potential difference).

Total Charge Through a Circuit Depends on Current and Time

1) The <u>current</u> is the <u>amount of charge</u> that flows through a circuit <u>every second</u>.

2) You can calculate current using <u>this equation</u>:

3) <u>Current</u>, I, is measured in <u>amperes</u> (A).
   <u>Charge</u>, Q, is measured in <u>coulombs</u> (C).
   <u>Time</u>, t, is measured in <u>seconds</u> (s).

4) <u>More charge</u> passes around the circuit when a <u>bigger current</u> flows.

$$\text{Current} = \frac{\text{Charge}}{\text{Time}}$$

$$I = \frac{Q}{t}$$

<u>EXAMPLE</u>: 600 C of charge passes through a cell in 4 minutes. How much current flows?

<u>ANSWER</u>: Time = 4 mins = 4 × 60 = 240 seconds
I = Q ÷ t = 600 ÷ 240 = 2.5 A

Potential Difference (P. D.) is the Work Done Per Unit Charge

1) <u>Potential difference</u> is the <u>work done per coulomb of charge</u> that passes between <u>two points</u> in an electrical circuit.

2) So, the potential difference across an electrical component is the <u>amount of energy</u> that is <u>transferred</u> by that electrical component <u>per unit of charge</u>.

3) You can calculate potential difference using this equation:

4) <u>V</u> is the <u>potential difference</u>, measured in <u>volts</u> (V).
   <u>W</u> is the <u>work done</u>, measured in <u>joules</u> (J).
   <u>Q</u> is the <u>charge</u>, measured in <u>coulombs</u> (C).

Potential difference is also called voltage.

$$\text{P.D.} = \frac{\text{Work done}}{\text{Charge}}$$

$$V = \frac{W}{Q}$$

I think it's about time you took charge...

Don't get confused by the words <u>voltage</u> and <u>potential difference</u> — they mean the <u>same thing</u>. Remember that the potential difference is how much work gets done (or how much energy is transferred) for every unit of charge.

Circuits — The Basics

Formulas are mighty pretty and all, but you might have to design some <u>electrical circuits</u> as well one day. For that you're going to need <u>circuit symbols</u>. Well, would you look at that... they're on this page.

Circuit Symbols <u>You Should Know</u> — <u>Learn Them Well</u>

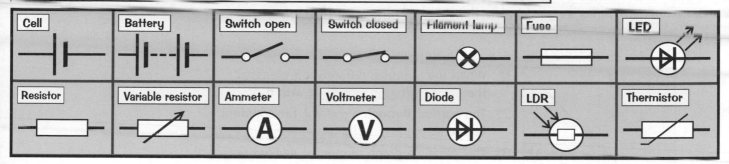

| Cell | Battery | Switch open | Switch closed | Filament lamp | Fuse | LED |
| Resistor | Variable resistor | Ammeter | Voltmeter | Diode | LDR | Thermistor |

The Standard Test Circuit

1) This is the circuit you use if you want to know the <u>resistance of a component</u>.
2) You find the resistance by measuring the <u>current through</u> and the <u>potential difference across</u> the component.
3) By <u>varying</u> (changing) the resistance in a circuit, you can measure the current through and the P.D. across a component, and <u>plot the values</u> in a graph.

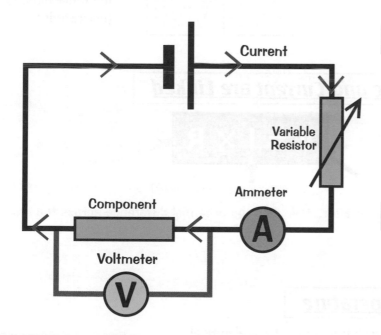

Current

Variable Resistor

Component

Ammeter

Voltmeter

The Ammeter

1) Measures the <u>current</u> (in <u>amps</u>) flowing through the component.
2) Must be placed <u>in series</u> (see p.92).
3) Can be put <u>anywhere</u> in series in the <u>main circuit</u>, but <u>never</u> in parallel like the voltmeter.

The Voltmeter

1) Measures the <u>potential difference</u> (in <u>volts</u>) across the component.
2) Must be placed <u>in parallel</u> (see p.93) around the <u>component</u> under test — <u>NOT</u> around the variable resistor or the battery!

<u>Measure gymnastics — use a vaultmeter...</u>

Weirdly, the <u>electrons</u> in circuits actually move from <u>–ve to +ve</u>, but scientists always think of <u>current</u> as flowing from <u>+ve to –ve</u>. It's just because that's how people thought of it before they found out about electrons, and it's stuck.

Resistance and V = I × R

With your <u>current</u> and your <u>potential difference</u> measured, you can now make some <u>sweet</u> graphs...

V-I Graphs show the Resistance of a Component

<u>Potential difference-current</u> (V-I) graphs show how the <u>current</u> through a component varies as you <u>change</u> the <u>potential difference</u> (P.D.).

Remember:
V = potential difference
and I = current

Different Resistors

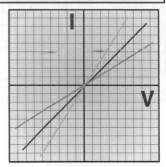

1) When the <u>potential difference increases</u>, the <u>current flowing increases</u> with it.
2) The current through a <u>resistor</u> (at constant temperature) is <u>directly proportional to P.D.</u>
3) This means a graph of <u>current</u> against <u>potential difference</u> for a resistor is a <u>straight line</u>.
4) The <u>steeper</u> the graph, the <u>lower</u> the resistance.

Filament Bulb

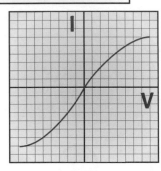

1) As the <u>temperature</u> of the filament <u>increases</u>, the <u>resistance increases</u>.
2) This is why there is a <u>curve</u>.

Diode

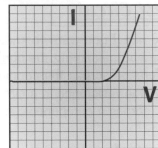

1) Current will only flow through a diode <u>in one direction</u> (forwards).
2) The diode has very <u>high resistance</u> in the other direction (backwards).

Resistance, Potential Difference and Current are Linked

You can calculate <u>potential difference</u> from the <u>resistance</u> and <u>current</u> using <u>this equation</u>:

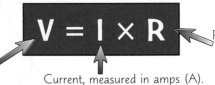

$$V = I \times R$$

Potential difference, measured in volts (V).

Current, measured in amps (A).

Resistance, measured in ohms (Ω).

EXAMPLE: 3 A of current passes through a 4 Ω resistor. Calculate the potential difference across the resistor.

ANSWER: V = I × R, so V = 3 × 4 = <u>12 V</u>.

Resistance Increases with Temperature

1) When an electrical charge flows through a resistor, some of the electrical energy is <u>transferred to heat energy</u> and the resistor gets <u>hot</u>.
2) When the resistor gets hot, its <u>resistance increases</u>, and <u>less current flows</u>.
3) For example, the <u>resistance</u> of a <u>filament bulb increases</u> as the <u>temperature</u> of the filament <u>increases</u>.

Learn this page — you know you can't resist...

You have to be able to understand potential difference-current graphs for bulbs, resistors and diodes for your exam. Remember — the <u>steeper</u> the <u>slope</u>, the <u>lower</u> the <u>resistance</u>. Make sure you're handy with that equation too.

Circuit Devices

You might know about bulbs, and you're switched on to switches, but they're not the whole story...
Make sure you know these circuit devices too — they're a little bit trickier.

Current Only Flows in One Direction through a LED

1) A light-emitting diode (LED) is a type of diode.
2) It emits light when a current flows through it in the forward direction.
3) LEDs are being used more and more as lighting, as they use a much smaller current than other forms of lighting.
4) LEDs can be used to show whether a current is flowing in a circuit.
5) They're often used in appliances (like TVs) to show that they are switched on.
6) They're also used for the numbers on digital clocks, in traffic lights and in remote controls.

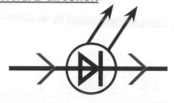

A Light-Dependent Resistor or "LDR" to You

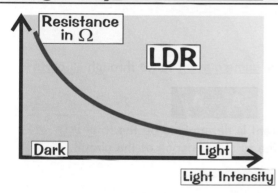

1) A light-dependent resistor (LDR) is a resistor that depends on the intensity (brightness) of light.
2) In bright light, the resistance falls.
3) In darkness, the resistance is highest.
4) They have lots of uses including automatic night lights, outdoor lighting and burglar detectors.

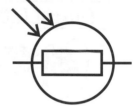

The Resistance of a Thermistor Decreases as Temperature Increases

1) A thermistor is a temperature dependent resistor.
2) In hot conditions, the resistance drops.
3) In cool conditions, the resistance goes up.
4) Thermistors make useful temperature detectors.
5) For example, they can be used for car engine temperature sensors and electronic thermostats (devices that control the temperature of a room or building).

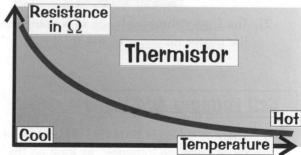

LDRs — Light-Dependent Rabbits...

LDRs are good triggers in security systems, because they can detect when the light intensity changes. So if a robber walks in front of a beam of light pointed at the LDR, the resistance shoots up and an alarm goes off.

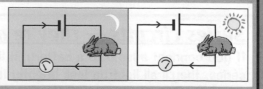

Series Circuits

You need to be able to tell the difference between series and parallel circuits <u>just by looking at them</u>. Read on.

Series Circuits — All or Nothing

1) In <u>series circuits</u>, the different components are connected <u>in a line</u>, <u>end to end</u>.

2) Only <u>voltmeters</u> are always connected <u>in parallel</u>, but they don't count as part of the circuit.

3) If you remove or disconnect <u>one</u> component, the circuit is <u>broken</u> and they all <u>stop</u>.

4) This is generally <u>not very handy</u>, and in practice <u>very few things</u> are connected in series.

Potential Difference is Shared:

1) In series circuits the <u>total P.D.</u> of the <u>supply</u> is <u>shared</u> between the various <u>components</u>.

2) So the <u>voltages</u> round a series circuit <u>always add up</u> to equal the <u>voltage</u> of the power supply:

$$V = V_1 + V_2 + ...$$

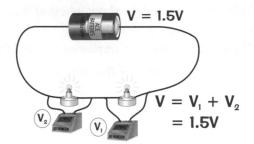

V = 1.5V

$V = V_1 + V_2$
$= 1.5V$

Current is the Same Everywhere:

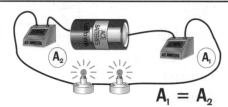

$A_1 = A_2$

1) In series circuits the <u>same current</u> flows through <u>all parts</u> of the circuit:

$$A_1 = A_2$$

2) The <u>size</u> of the current is determined by the <u>total P.D.</u> of the supply and the <u>total resistance</u> of the circuit.

Resistance Adds Up:

1) In series circuits the <u>total resistance</u> is just the <u>sum</u> of all the resistances:

$$R = R_1 + R_2 + R_3$$

2) The <u>bigger</u> the <u>resistance</u> of a component, the bigger its <u>share</u> of the <u>total P.D.</u>

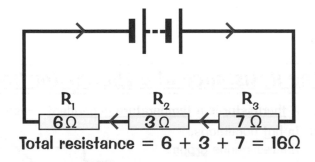

R_1	R_2	R_3
6 Ω	3 Ω	7 Ω

Total resistance = 6 + 3 + 7 = 16Ω

Cell Voltages Add Up:

1) There is a bigger potential difference when more cells are in series, as long as the cells are all <u>connected</u> the <u>same way</u>.

2) For example, when two 12 V cells are <u>connected in series</u> they supply 24 V <u>between them</u>.

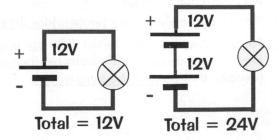

Total = 12V   Total = 24V

Series circuits — they're no laughing matter...

If you connect a lamp to a battery, it lights up with a certain brightness. If you add more identical lamps in series, they'll all light up <u>less brightly</u> than before because the voltage is <u>shared out</u> between all of them.

Parallel Circuits

Parallel circuits are more common than series circuits in real life. The circuits in your house will all be parallel.

Parallel Circuits — More Useful than Series Circuits

1) In parallel circuits, each component is separately connected to the positive and negative of the supply.
2) If you remove or disconnect one of them, it will hardly affect the others at all.
3) This is obviously how most things must be connected, for example in cars and in household electrics. You have to be able to switch everything on and off separately.

P.D. is the Same Across All Components:

1) In parallel circuits all components get the full P.D. of the supply.
2) So the potential difference is the same across all components:

$$V_1 = V_2 = V_3$$

3) This means that identical bulbs connected in parallel will all be at the same brightness.

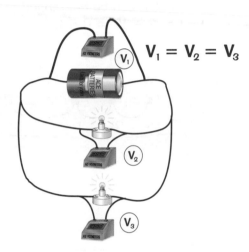

$$V_1 = V_2 = V_3$$

Current is Shared Between Branches:

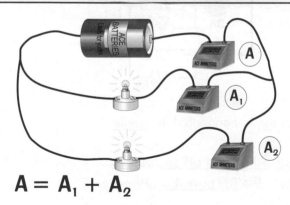

$$A = A_1 + A_2$$

1) In parallel circuits the total current flowing around the circuit is equal to the total of all the currents through the separate components.

$$A = A_1 + A_2 + ...$$

2) In a parallel circuit, there are junctions where the current either splits or rejoins.
3) The total current going into a junction has to equal the total current leaving.
4) If two identical components are connected in parallel then the same current will flow through each component.

A current shared — is a current halved...

Parallel circuits might look a bit scarier than series ones, but they're much more useful.
And you don't have to know as many equations for them (yay!). Remember: each branch has the same voltage across it, and the total current is equal to the sum of the currents through each of the branches.

Series and Parallel Circuits — Examples

It's <u>not enough</u> to know how circuits work in theory. You need to be able to calculate the currents, potential differences and resistances in a <u>range of examples</u>. It <u>will</u> be on the exam, so work through <u>these examples</u> now.

Example on Series Circuits

1) <u>Potential differences</u> add to equal the <u>source P.D.</u>:
   1.5 + 2 + 2.5 = 6 V

2) <u>Total resistance</u> is the sum of the resistances in the circuit: 3 + 4 + 5 = 12 Ω

3) <u>Current</u> flowing through all parts of the circuit can be found using the equation V = I × R, where V is potential difference, I is current and R is resistance:
   V = I × R can be rearranged to I = V ÷ R
   So I = 6 ÷ 12 = 0.5 A

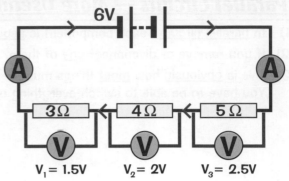

$V_1 = 1.5V$ $V_2 = 2V$ $V_3 = 2.5V$

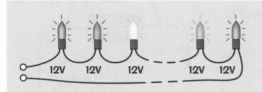

<u>Christmas fairy lights</u> are about the <u>only</u> real-life example of things connected in <u>series</u>, and they can be a right <u>pain</u> when the <u>whole lot go out</u> when one bulb breaks.

Example on Parallel Circuits

1) The <u>P.D.</u> across each resistor in the circuit is the same as the <u>supply P.D.</u> Each voltmeter will read 6 V.

2) The <u>current</u> through each <u>resistor</u> will be <u>different</u> because they have different values of <u>resistance</u>.

3) The current through the <u>battery</u> is the same as the <u>sum</u> of the other currents in the branches.
   $A_1 = A_2 + A_3 + A_4 \Rightarrow A_1 = 1.5 + 3 + 1 = 5.5$ A

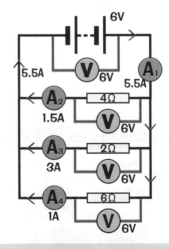

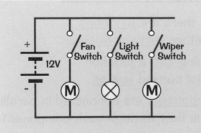

Everything electrical in a <u>car</u> is connected in <u>parallel</u>. This is so that:

1) Everything can be <u>turned on and off separately</u>.

2) Everything always gets the <u>full potential difference</u> from the battery.

Ⓜ is the symbol for a motor.

In a parallel universe — my car would start...

A lot of fairy lights are actually done on a <u>parallel</u> circuit these days — they have a transformer that brings the voltage down, so the lights can still be diddy but it doesn't matter if one of them blows. Cunning.

Well done — you've made it to the end of the section. There are loads of bits and bobs and electricity which you have to learn. The best way to find out what you know is to get in to these lovely revision questions, which you're going to really enjoy (honest)...

1) What's the difference between speed and velocity?

2) What does the gradient on a distance-time graph show?

3) What is acceleration?

4)* Write down the formula for acceleration. What's the acceleration of a soggy pea flicked from rest to a speed of 14 m/s in 0.4 seconds?

5) Explain the difference between mass and weight. What units are they measured in?

6) Explain what is meant by a "resultant force".

7) If an object has zero resultant force on it, can it be moving? Can it be accelerating?

8)* Write down the formula for resultant force and acceleration.
A resultant force of 30 N pushes a trolley of mass 4 kg. What will its acceleration be?

9)* A yeti pushes a tree with a force of 120 N. What is the size of the reaction force that the Yeti feels pushing back at him?

10) How does the air resistance acting on a car change as the car speeds up?

11) What is "terminal velocity"?

12) Give two factors that affect the braking distance of a car.

13)* Write down the formula for work done. A crazy dog drags a big branch 12 m over the next-door neighbour's front lawn, pulling with a force of 535 N. How much work was done?

14)* A 4 kg cheese is taken 30 m up a hill.
If g = 10 N/kg, how much gravitational potential energy does the cheese have at the top of the hill?

15)* What's the formula for kinetic energy? Find the kinetic energy of a 78 kg sheep moving at 23 m/s.

16)* Calculate the kinetic energy of the same 78 kg sheep just as she hits the floor after falling through 20 m. (Use g = 10 N/kg.)

17) Write down the equation that links the force on a spring and its extension.

18) Describe how adding a roof box would affect the top speed of a car. Explain your answer.
Hint: think about how the roof box will change the shape of the car.

19) Write down the formula for momentum.

20) What is the advantage of using regenerative braking systems?

21) Explain in terms of momentum change how crumple zones help protect passengers in a crash.

22) Explain in terms of energy change how seat belts protect passengers in a crash.

23) What causes the build-up of static electricity? Which particles move when static builds up?

24) True or false: the greater the resistance of an electrical component, the smaller the current that flows through it.

25)* 240 C of charge is carried though a wire in a circuit in one minute.
How much current has flowed through the wire?

26) What formula relates work done, potential difference and charge?

27) Draw a diagram of the circuit that you would use to find the resistance of a motor.

28) Sketch typical potential difference-current graphs for:
a) a resistor, b) a diode. Explain the shape of each graph.

29)* What potential difference is needed to push 2 A of current through a 0.6 Ω resistor?

30) Give three uses of LEDs.

31) Describe how the resistance of an LDR varies with light intensity. Describe one use of an LDR.

32)* A 4 Ω bulb and a 6 Ω bulb are connected in series with a 12 V battery.
a) How much current flows through the 4 W bulb?
b) What is the potential difference over the 6 W bulb?
c) What would the potential difference over the 6 W bulb be if the two bulbs were connected in parallel?

Mains Electricity

Electric current is the flow of electric charges. To transfer energy, it doesn't matter which way the charges are going. That's why an alternating current works. Read on to find out more...

Mains Supply is AC, Battery Supply is DC

1) The UK mains supply is approximately 230 volts.

2) It is an alternating current (a.c.) supply.

3) This means the current is constantly changing direction.

4) The frequency of the a.c. mains supply is 50 cycles per second or 50 Hz (hertz).

5) Cells and batteries supply direct current (d.c.).

6) This just means that the current from batteries always keeps flowing in the same direction.

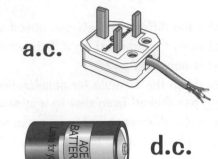

a.c.

d.c.

Electricity Supplies Can Be Shown on an Oscilloscope Screen

1) An oscilloscope is basically a snazzy voltmeter.

2) If you plug an electricity supply into an oscilloscope, you get a 'trace' on the screen.

3) This shows how the potential difference of the supply changes with time.

4) For an a.c. supply, the trace goes up and down in a regular pattern.

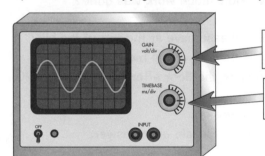

The GAIN dial controls how many volts each centimetre division (each big square on the grid) represents on the vertical axis.

The TIMEBASE dial controls how many milliseconds (1 ms = 0.001 s) each division represents on the horizontal axis.

Learn How to Read an Oscilloscope Trace

1) The vertical height of the a.c. trace at any point shows the input potential difference at that point.

2) The distance between the time line and the highest point of the trace shows the peak potential difference of the a.c. supply.

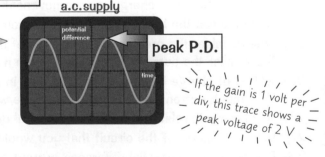

a.c. supply

potential difference

time

peak P.D.

If the gain is 1 volt per div, this trace shows a peak voltage of 2 V

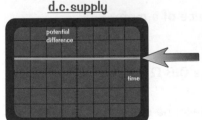

d.c. supply

potential difference

time

3) If you plug in a d.c. supply, the trace you get is just a straight line.

4) For d.c., the potential difference is just the distance from the straight line trace to the centre line.

I wish my bank account had a gain dial...

It doesn't matter if the electrical charges are travelling in one direction or moving backwards and forwards. So long as they're moving they can transfer electrical energy to other forms. This is why alternating current works.

Electricity in the Home

Now then, did you know... electricity is <u>dangerous</u>. It can kill you. Well just watch out for it, that's all.

Watch out for Electrical Dangers in your Home

Learn these nine examples:

1) <u>Long cables</u>.
2) <u>Frayed cables</u>.
3) <u>Cables</u> in contact with something <u>hot</u> or <u>wet</u>.
4) <u>Water near sockets</u>.
5) <u>Shoving</u> things into sockets.

6) <u>Damaged plugs</u>.
7) <u>Too many</u> plugs into one socket.
8) Lighting sockets <u>without bulbs in</u>.
9) Appliances without their <u>covers</u> on.

Most Cables Have Three Separate Wires

1) Most electrical appliances are connected to the mains supply by a <u>cable</u> and a <u>three-pin plug</u>.

2) Most cables are <u>three-core</u> cables. This just means they have <u>three wires</u> inside them.

3) The brown <u>LIVE WIRE</u> in a mains supply alternates between a <u>HIGH POSITIVE AND NEGATIVE POTENTIAL DIFFERENCE</u>.

4) The blue <u>NEUTRAL WIRE</u> is always at <u>0V</u>.

5) Electricity normally flows in and out through the live and neutral wires only.

6) The green and yellow <u>EARTH WIRE</u> is for protecting the wiring, and for safety (see next page).

live wire (alternating between positive and negative high potential difference)

neutral wire (0V)

earth wire

insulating cover

Plugs and Cables — Learn the Safety Features

Get the Wiring Right

1) The <u>right coloured wire</u> is connected to each pin, and <u>firmly screwed</u> in.

2) <u>No bare wires</u> showing inside the plug.

3) <u>Cable grip</u> tightly fastened over the cable <u>outer layer</u>.

Plug Features

1) The <u>metal parts</u> are made of copper or brass because these are <u>very good conductors</u>.

2) The case, cable grip and cable insulation are made of <u>rubber</u> or <u>plastic</u> because they're really good <u>insulators</u>, and <u>flexible</u> too.

3) This all keeps the electricity flowing <u>where it should</u>.

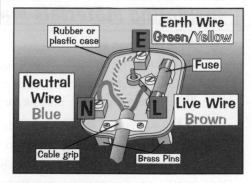

Rubber or plastic case

Earth Wire Green/Yellow

E

Fuse

Neutral Wire Blue

N L

Live Wire Brown

Cable grip

Brass Pins

CGP books are ACE — well, I had to get a plug in somewhere...

Not only is it important to learn how to <u>wire a plug</u> for passing your exam, its also useful for when you need to do it in real life. I know — shocking right? Well hopefully it won't be if you do it correctly...

Physics 2b — Electricity and the Atom

Fuses and Earthing

Questions about fuses are an exam favourite because they cover a whole barrel of fun — electrical current, resistance, energy transfers and electrical safety. Learn this page and make sure you've got it sussed.

Earthing and Fuses Help Keep you Safe

The earth wire and fuse (or circuit breaker — see next page) are put in electrical appliances to make them safe and protect the electrical wiring from getting fried. They work together like this:

1) Say there's a fault, and the live wire somehow touches the metal case.

2) Because the case is earthed, the fault suddenly causes a large current to flow in through the live wire, through the case and out down the earth wire.

3) This surge in current melts the fuse when the amount of current is greater than the fuse rating.

4) This cuts off the live supply and breaks the circuit. This makes it impossible to get an electric shock from the case.

5) It also lowers the risk of a fire being caused by the heating effect of a large current.

6) The larger the current, the thicker the cable you need to carry it.

7) That means the fuse rating needed for cables usually increases with cable thickness too.

Insulating Materials Make Appliances "Double Insulated"

1) All appliances with metal cases are usually earthed to reduce the danger of getting an electric shock.

2) Earthing just means the case must be attached to an earth wire. This means the case can never become live.

3) If the appliance has a plastic casing and no metal parts showing then it's said to be double insulated.

4) The case is insulating, so even if the live wire touches it, it won't become live.

5) That means anything with double insulation doesn't need an earth wire — just a live and neutral.

6) Cables that only carry the live and neutral wires are known as two-core cables.

Remember: an insulator is a material that current can't flow through easily.

Why are earth wires green and yellow — when mud is brown..?

All these safety features mean it's pretty difficult to get electrocuted by modern appliances. But that's only so long as they are in good condition and you're not doing something really stupid. Watch out for frayed wires, don't overload plugs, and for goodness sake don't use a knife to get toast out of a toaster when it is switched on.

Fuses and Earthing

Fuses have saved countless lives over the years by <u>breaking the circuit</u> when too large a current flows. But it can be <u>annoying</u> when you have to replace them. You can use <u>circuit breakers</u> to get around this problem...

Circuit Breakers can be used Instead of Fuses

1) When <u>circuit breakers</u> detect a <u>surge</u> in <u>current</u> in a circuit, they <u>break</u> the circuit by <u>opening</u> a <u>switch</u>.

2) A circuit breaker (and the circuit they're in) can easily be <u>reset</u> by flicking the <u>switch</u> closed again.

3) This makes them <u>more convenient</u> than fuses — which have to be <u>replaced</u> once they've melted.

4) They are, however, a lot <u>more expensive</u> to buy than fuses.

5) One type of circuit breaker used instead of a fuse and an earth wire is a <u>Residual Current Circuit Breaker</u> (<u>RCCB</u>):

> 1) Normally <u>exactly the same</u> current flows through the <u>live</u> and <u>neutral</u> wires.
>
> 2) If somebody touches the live wire, a current will flow through them to the earth.
>
> 3) This means the neutral wire carries <u>less</u> current than the live wire.
>
> 4) The RCCB detects this <u>difference</u> in current and quickly cuts off the power by <u>opening a switch</u>.
>
> 5) They also operate much <u>faster</u> than fuses. They break the circuit as soon as there is a current surge so no time is wasted waiting for the current to melt a fuse. This makes them <u>safer</u>.
>
> 6) RCCBs even work for <u>small current changes</u> that might not be large enough to melt a fuse. This means RCCBs are better at <u>protecting against electrocution</u>.

Electrical Power and Fuse Ratings

1) The formula for <u>electrical power</u> (P) is:
2) Power is measured in watts (W).

POWER = CURRENT × POTENTIAL DIFFERENCE

$$P = I \times V$$

> <u>EXAMPLE:</u> A kettle uses mains voltage (230 V) and a current of 12 A. What is its power rating?
>
> <u>ANSWER:</u> $P = I \times V = 12 \times 230 = 2760$ W.

3) Most electrical goods show their <u>power rating</u> and <u>potential difference</u> (voltage) <u>rating</u>.

4) To work out the size of the <u>fuse</u> needed, you need to work out the <u>current</u> that the item will normally use. You can do this by rearranging the power equation $I = P \div V$.

Don't worry about rearranging equations. If you need to use this equation you'll be given it.

5) The rating of a fuse is a current <u>above which</u> the fuse will <u>melt</u>.

6) The fuse you use should be rated <u>just higher</u> than the current the appliance needs.

7) This way, enough current can flow to make the appliance <u>work</u>, but if any more flows you won't get electrocuted.

> <u>EXAMPLE:</u> A hair dryer is rated at 230 V, 1000 W. Should a 3 A, 4 A, 5 A or 6 A fuse be used in the hair dryer?
>
> <u>ANSWER:</u> $I = P \div V = 1000 \div 230 = 4.3$ A. Normally, the fuse should be rated just a little higher than the normal current, so a 5 A fuse is ideal for this one.

You have the power — now use your potential...

It's really important that the <u>right fuses</u> are fitted in your appliances. <u>Too low</u> a fuse rating and your appliances <u>won't work</u> because the fuse will <u>melt</u> straight away. <u>Too high</u> a fuse and you're <u>at risk</u> if something goes wrong.

Energy and Power in Circuits

Electricity is just another form of <u>energy</u> — which means that it is always <u>conserved</u>.

Energy is Transferred from Cells and Other Sources

1) Anything which <u>supplies electricity</u> is also supplying <u>energy</u>.

2) Cells, batteries, generators, etc. all <u>transfer energy</u> to components in the circuit:

<u>Motion</u>: motors	<u>Light</u>: light bulbs	<u>Heat</u>: Hairdriers/kettles	<u>Sound</u>: speakers

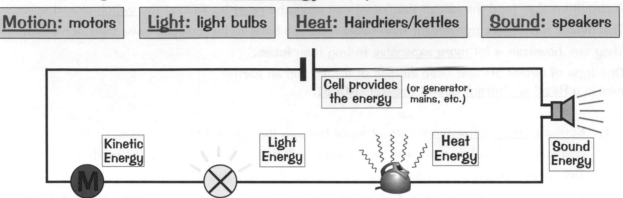

Cell provides the energy (or generator, mains, etc.)

Kinetic Energy

Light Energy

Heat Energy

Sound Energy

3) Anything with a <u>resistance</u> gets <u>hot</u> when a current flows through it (see p.90).

4) <u>Filament bulbs</u> work by passing a current through a very <u>thin wire</u>, heating it up so much that it glows.

5) This means filament bulbs <u>waste</u> a lot of energy as <u>heat</u>.

If an Appliance is Efficient it Wastes Less Energy

1) When you buy electrical appliances you can choose to buy ones that are more <u>energy efficient</u>.

2) These appliances transfer more of their <u>total electrical energy output</u> to useful energy.

Remember: efficiency = useful energy out ÷ total energy in.

Not an energy efficient lamp.

3) For example, less energy is wasted as heat in power-saving lamps such as <u>compact fluorescent lamps</u> (CFLs) and <u>light-emitting diodes</u> (p.91) than in ordinary filament bulbs.

4) Unfortunately, they do <u>cost more to buy</u>.

5) Over time, the money you <u>save</u> on your electricity bills pays you back for the initial cost.

Power of Appliances

1) It's not only efficiency that matters when choosing your appliances — the <u>power rating</u> matters too.

2) Power is the <u>rate</u> at which <u>energy is transferred</u> by an appliance and is given by this equation:

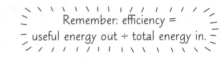

Power = Energy Transferred ÷ time

3) The power of an appliance is the <u>energy</u> that it uses <u>per second</u>.

4) Power, P, is measured in <u>watts</u> (W). Energy, E, is measured in <u>joules</u> (J), and t is the time in <u>seconds</u> (s).

$$P = \frac{E}{t}$$

5) If you want a really bright light bulb, then a 100 W one will glow brighter than a 60 W one. But it will use <u>more energy</u> over a given time.

My power is rated A for Awesome...

The equation for <u>power</u> is one you're really gonna need for the exam, so make sure you've got it hard-wired into your memory. Remember: power is energy transferred per second. Power is energy transferred per second. Power is energy transferred per second...

Atomic Structure

Scientists had thought matter was made up of <u>tiny balls</u> (atoms) for centuries. It's only been in the last hundred years or so that we've started to get a <u>real idea</u> of what these tiny particles are made of...

Rutherford Scattering and the End of the Plum Pudding

1) In 1897 <u>J J Thomson</u> discovered <u>electrons</u>.

2) Thomson suggested that <u>atoms</u> were <u>spheres (balls) of positive charge</u> with tiny negative electrons <u>stuck in them</u> like plums in a <u>plum pudding</u>.

3) That "plum pudding" theory didn't last very long though...

4) In 1909 <u>Rutherford</u> and <u>Marsden</u> tried firing a beam of <u>alpha particles</u> (see p.103) at <u>thin gold foil</u>.

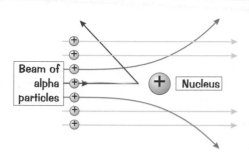

5) They expected that the <u>positively charged</u> alpha particles would be <u>slightly deflected</u> (made to change direction) by the electrons in the plum pudding atoms.

6) But most of the alpha particles just went <u>straight through</u>. This showed that most of an atom is just <u>empty space</u>.

7) And sometimes an alpha particle would come <u>straight back at them</u>. Rutherford and Marsden realised this meant that <u>most of the mass</u> of the atom was at the <u>centre</u> in a <u>tiny nucleus</u>.

8) They also realised that the nucleus must have a <u>positive charge</u>, since it <u>repelled</u> the positive alpha particles.

Rutherford and Marsden Came Up with the Nuclear Model of the Atom

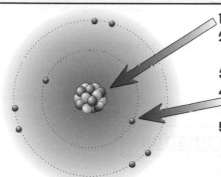

1) The <u>nucleus</u> is <u>tiny</u> but it makes up most of the <u>mass</u> of the atom.

2) It contains <u>protons</u> (which are <u>positively charged</u>) and <u>neutrons</u> (which are <u>neutral</u>) — which means it has an overall positive charge.

3) The rest of the atom is mostly <u>empty space</u>.

4) The <u>negative electrons</u> whizz round the outside of the nucleus really fast. They give the atom its <u>overall size</u>.

5) Learn the <u>relative charges</u> and <u>masses</u> of each particle:

PARTICLE	MASS	CHARGE
Proton	1	+1
Neutron	1	0
Electron	$\frac{1}{2000}$	-1

The <u>relative</u> charge (or mass) is the charge (or mass) of one particle compared to the others.

Number of Protons Equals Number of Electrons

1) Atoms have <u>no charge</u> overall.

2) The <u>charge</u> on an electron is the <u>same</u> size as the charge on a <u>proton</u> — but <u>opposite</u>.

3) This means the <u>number</u> of <u>protons</u> always equals the <u>number</u> of <u>electrons</u> in a <u>neutral atom</u>.

4) If some electrons are <u>added or removed</u> from an atom, it becomes a <u>charged ion</u>.

And I always thought Kate Moss was the best model...

The nuclear model is just <u>one way of thinking about</u> the atom. It works really well for explaining lots of stuff, but it's certainly not the whole story. There are other models that are used to explain different parts of science.

Atoms and Radiation

Now you've got your head around the structure of the atom, stuff starts to get real interesting...

Isotopes are Different Forms of the Same Element

1) <u>Atoms</u> of an element always have the <u>same</u> number of <u>protons</u>, but can have a <u>different</u> number of <u>neutrons</u>.
2) <u>Atomic number</u> is the <u>number of protons</u> in an atom.
3) <u>Mass number</u> is the <u>number of protons</u> + the <u>number of neutrons</u> in an atom.
4) The <u>different</u> forms of the <u>same element</u> are called <u>isotopes</u>.
5) Isotopes have the <u>same atomic number</u>, but <u>different mass numbers</u>.
6) <u>Carbon-12</u> and <u>carbon-14</u> are good examples of isotopes:

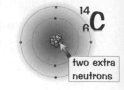

two extra neutrons

Radioactivity is a Totally Random Process

1) Some particles are <u>radioactive</u>.
2) This means they <u>decay</u> into <u>other elements</u> and <u>give out radiation</u>.
3) <u>Unstable isotopes</u> undergo <u>radioactive decay</u>.
4) <u>Radioactive substances</u> give out radiation from the nuclei of their atoms — <u>no matter what is done to them</u>. This process is entirely <u>random</u>.
5) This means that if you have 1000 radioactive nuclei, you can't say when <u>any one of them</u> is going to decay. You can't do anything <u>to make a decay happen either</u>.

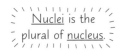

Nuclei is the plural of <u>nucleus</u>.

Background Radiation Comes from Many Sources

1) You're always exposed to a <u>small amount</u> of <u>radiation</u>. This radiation is <u>background radiation</u>.
2) The background radiation we receive comes from:
   a) <u>Natural</u> sources — <u>rocks</u> under our feet and radiation from <u>space</u>, known as <u>cosmic rays</u>.
   b) Radiation due to <u>man-made sources</u> — <u>fallout</u> (left over radiation) from <u>nuclear weapons tests</u> and <u>nuclear accidents</u>.

Radiation Dose Depends on Location and Occupation

1) The amount of radiation you're exposed to is called your <u>radiation dose</u>.
2) Radiation dose depends on the <u>type</u> and <u>amount of radiation</u> you've been exposed to.
3) The <u>higher</u> the radiation dose, the <u>more at risk</u> you are of <u>getting cancer</u> (see p.105).
4) Your radiation dose can be affected by your <u>location</u> (where you are) and <u>occupation</u> (job).
5) Certain <u>underground rocks</u> can cause higher levels of radiation at the Earth's <u>surface</u>. This varies from place to place.
6) <u>Underground</u> (in <u>mines</u>) the levels of radiation are even higher because of the surrounding <u>rocks</u>.
7) People who work underground, for example <u>uranium miners</u>, are exposed to more radiation and have to wear <u>protective clothing</u>.
8) <u>High up</u> in the atmosphere the level of background radiation is <u>higher</u>. This is because there are more <u>cosmic rays</u>. This means <u>pilots</u> get a higher than normal radiation dose.
9) People who <u>work with radiation</u> such as <u>radiographers</u> in hospitals or <u>nuclear power station workers</u> will have a higher than normal radiation dose because of their jobs.

Completely random — just like your revision shouldn't be...

The number of <u>protons</u> decides what <u>element</u> something is, and the number of <u>neutrons</u> decides what <u>isotope</u> it is.

Ionising Radiation

Alpha (α) Beta (β) Gamma (γ) — there are three types of radiation for you to learn here. And they're all <u>ionising</u>.

An Alpha Particle is a Helium Nucleus

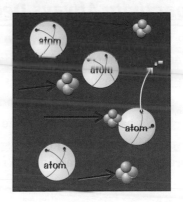

1) An alpha particle is <u>two neutrons</u> and <u>two protons</u>.

2) So an alpha particle is the same as a <u>helium nucleus</u>.

3) They are relatively <u>big</u> and <u>heavy</u> and <u>slow moving</u>.

4) They <u>don't penetrate</u> (travel) very far into materials and are <u>stopped quickly</u>, even when travelling through <u>air</u>.

5) Because they're large they <u>bash into</u> a lot of atoms and <u>knock electrons off them</u> before they slow down.

6) This creates lots of ions — they are <u>strongly ionising</u>.

Beta Particles are Electrons

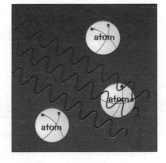

1) Beta particles are <u>electrons</u> — they are <u>small</u> and <u>negatively</u> charged.

2) They <u>penetrate further</u> into materials than alpha particles.

3) But they don't penetrate as far as than <u>gamma rays</u>.

4) They have a <u>long range</u> (they can travel very far) in air.

5) They are <u>moderately ionising</u> — they ionise <u>more</u> than <u>gamma rays</u>, but <u>not as much</u> as <u>alpha particles</u>.

Gamma Rays are Very Short Wavelength EM Waves

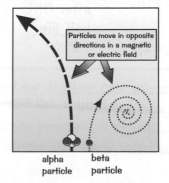

1) Gamma rays are <u>electromagnetic (EM) waves</u>.

2) They <u>penetrate far into materials</u> without being stopped and pass <u>straight through air</u>.

3) They are <u>weakly</u> ionising because they tend to <u>pass through</u> materials rather than collide with atoms.

4) Eventually they <u>hit something</u> and do <u>damage</u>.

Alpha and Beta Particles are Affected by Electric and Magnetic Fields

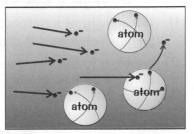

1) When travelling through a <u>magnetic</u> or <u>electric field</u>, both alpha and beta particles will be <u>deflected</u> — they will change direction.

2) Alpha and beta particles are deflected in <u>opposite directions</u> (because of their opposite charges).

3) Alpha particles are deflected <u>less</u> than beta particles.

4) <u>Gamma radiation doesn't get deflected</u> by electric or magnetic fields.

Particles move in opposite directions in a magnetic or electric field

alpha particle

beta particle

I once beta particle — it cried for ages...

Gamma radiation doesn't get deflected because it is an <u>EM wave</u> and <u>doesn't</u> have a <u>charge</u>.
Alpha and beta radiation are <u>charged particles</u>, which is one reason why they are so <u>ionising</u>.

Half-Life

How <u>radioactive</u> a substance is can be measured by its <u>half life</u>. Read on...

Radioactivity Always Decreases Over Time

1) Each time a <u>decay</u> happens, one more <u>radioactive nucleus</u> disappears.
2) The <u>activity</u> of a sample is number of radioactive nuclei that decay in a period of time.
3) The <u>unit</u> for measuring <u>activity</u> is the <u>becquerel</u> (Bq). 1 Bq means <u>one nucleus decays per second</u>.
4) As the <u>radioactive nuclei</u> all steadily disappear, the <u>activity</u> will <u>decrease</u>.
5) The <u>older</u> a sample becomes, the <u>less radiation</u> it will emit (give out).
6) <u>How quickly</u> the activity <u>decreases</u> varies a lot. For <u>some</u> substances it takes <u>a fraction of a second</u> before nearly all the radioactive nuclei have <u>decayed</u>. For others it can take <u>millions of years</u>.

Half-Life Gives us a Measure of Activity

1) The <u>activity</u> of a radioactive substance <u>never reaches zero</u>, which means it can be difficult to measure.
2) We have to use the idea of <u>half-life</u> to measure how quickly the activity <u>drops off</u>.

> **HALF-LIFE** is the **AVERAGE TIME** it takes for the **NUMBER OF NUCLEI** in a **RADIOACTIVE ISOTOPE SAMPLE** to **HALVE**.

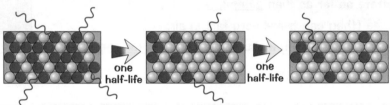

3) A <u>short half-life</u> means the <u>activity falls quickly</u> — <u>lots</u> of the nuclei decay <u>quickly</u>.
4) A <u>long half-life</u> means the activity <u>falls more slowly</u> — <u>most</u> of the nuclei don't decay <u>for a long time</u>.

Do Half-life Questions Step by Step

1) Half-life is maybe a little confusing, but exam calculations are <u>straightforward</u>.
2) You need to them slowly, <u>STEP BY STEP</u>. Like this one:

> <u>EXAMPLE</u>: The activity of a radioisotope is 640 Bq.
>   120 minutes later it has fallen to 80 Bq. Find the half-life of the sample.
>
> <u>ANSWER</u>: You must go through it in <u>short simple steps</u> like this:
>
> | INITIAL
 <u>count:</u> | | after ONE
 <u>half-life:</u> | | after TWO
 <u>half-lives:</u> | | after THREE
 <u>half-lives:</u> |
> |---|---|---|---|---|---|---|
> | 640 | (÷2)→ | 320 | (÷2)→ | 160 | (÷2)→ | 80 |

3) By using this <u>step-by-step method</u>, we know it takes <u>three half-lives</u> for the activity to fall from 640 to 80.
4) That means <u>120 minutes</u> is the same as three half-lives.
5) So to find one <u>half-life</u>, divide 120 minutes by 3:   120 mins ÷ 3 = <u>40 minutes</u>.

Half-life of a box of chocolates — about five minutes...

Half-life is a <u>pretty tricky</u> idea to understand. Take your time over this page and go through the example <u>nice and slowly</u> and you'll soon be able to zip through half-life calculations come exam time.

Uses of Radiation

Radiation can be jolly <u>useful</u>, don't you know. Read all about it here chaps...

Smoke Detectors — Use α-Radiation

1) A <u>weak</u> source of <u>alpha</u> radiation is placed in the smoke detector.

2) The source causes <u>ionisation</u>, and the ions form a <u>current</u>.

3) If there is a fire then smoke will <u>absorb</u> the radiation.

4) This causes the current to stop and the <u>alarm sounds</u>.

Tracers in Medicine — Always Short Half-Life β or γ -Emitters

1) Certain <u>radioactive isotopes</u> are used as <u>tracers</u> for medicine.

2) A patient has the tracer <u>injected</u> (or they can just <u>swallow</u> them).

3) Where the tracer goes in the <u>body</u> can be followed using a <u>detector</u>.

4) <u>Iodine-131</u> is often used as a tracer. It can be used to show whether the thyroid gland is <u>taking in iodine</u> as it should.

5) <u>All tracers</u> must be <u>GAMMA or BETA</u> emitters (never alpha). These types of radiation are able to <u>pass out of the body</u>.

6) They should have a <u>short half-life</u>, so that the radioactivity inside the patient <u>quickly disappears</u>.

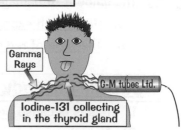

Gamma Rays

G-M tubes Ltd.

Iodine-131 collecting in the thyroid gland

Some Cancer Treatment Uses γ-Rays

1) High doses of gamma rays will <u>kill all living cells</u>.

2) This means they can be used to <u>treat cancers</u>.

3) The gamma rays have to be <u>directed carefully</u> at the <u>cancer cells</u>.

4) This way the cancer cells can be killed without damaging too many <u>normal cells</u>.

Food can be Sterilised Using γ-Rays

1) <u>Gamma rays</u> can be used to <u>kill</u> the <u>microbes</u> (germs) in food.

2) This is called <u>sterilisation</u>.

3) It is used because it keeps the food <u>fresh for longer</u>.

4) The food is <u>not</u> radioactive afterwards, so it's <u>safe</u> to eat.

5) <u>Hospital tools</u> can be <u>sterilised</u> in just the same way.

6) The radioactive source used for this needs to be a <u>very strong</u> emitter of <u>gamma rays</u>.

7) It should have a <u>reasonably long half-life</u> (at least several months) so that it doesn't need <u>replacing</u> too often.

unsterilised

Gamma source

sterilised

<u>Ionising radiation — just what the doctor ordered...</u>

Radiation has many important uses, especially in <u>medicine</u>. Make sure you know the <u>type</u> of radiation needed for each use of radioactivity. It's the sort of thing that examiners just love to test you on.

Radioactivity Safety

So, radiation is <u>dangerous</u>. Got it? Here's a page on the <u>nasty</u> things it can do and how to be <u>safe</u> when using it.

Radiation Harms Living Cells

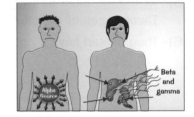

1) <u>Alpha</u>, <u>beta</u> and <u>gamma</u> radiation can <u>enter</u> <u>living cells</u> and <u>collide with</u> (hit) <u>molecules</u>.

2) These collisions cause <u>ionisation</u>, which <u>damages or destroys</u> the <u>molecules</u>.

3) If cells are <u>slightly damaged</u>, they can become <u>mutant cells</u> which <u>divide uncontrollably</u>. This is <u>cancer</u>.

4) <u>Higher doses</u> of radiation <u>kill cells completely</u>, which can make you feel <u>very ill</u>. This is called <u>radiation sickness</u>.

5) The amount of damage done depends on two things:

    a) <u>How much exposure</u> you have to the radiation (how much radiation hits you).

    b) The <u>type of radiation</u> you are exposed to (see below).

Outside the Body, β and γ-Sources are the Most Dangerous

1) This is because <u>beta and gamma</u> can get <u>inside</u> to the <u>organs</u>.

2) Alpha is much less dangerous because it <u>can't penetrate</u> (get through) the <u>skin</u>.

Inside the Body, an α-Source is the Most Dangerous

1) <u>Inside the body</u> alpha sources do lots of damage in <u>one area</u>.

2) Beta and gamma sources are <u>less dangerous</u> inside the body. They mostly <u>pass straight out</u> of the body without doing much damage.

You Need to Learn About These Safety Precautions

Radioactive materials need to be handled <u>carefully</u>.
Here are <u>some safety measures</u> that should be taken when <u>handling radioactive materials</u>:

1) Use radioactive sources for as <u>short a time</u> as possible when doing experiments so your <u>exposure</u> is kept as low as possible.

2) <u>Never</u> allow <u>skin contact</u> with a source (don't touch it). Always handle with <u>tongs</u>.

3) Hold the source at <u>arm's length</u> to keep it <u>as far</u> from the body <u>as possible</u>.

4) Keep the source <u>pointing away</u> from the body and <u>don't look straight at it</u>.

5) <u>Lead</u> absorbs all three types of radiation (though a lot of it is needed to stop gamma radiation completely). <u>Always</u> store radioactive sources in a <u>lead box</u> and put them away <u>as soon</u> as the experiment is <u>over</u>.

6) People who work with radiation <u>every day</u> wear <u>lead aprons</u> and stand behind <u>lead screens</u> for extra protection because they absorb the radiation.

7) When someone needs an X-ray, only the area of the body that <u>needs to be X-rayed</u> is exposed to radiation. The rest of the body is <u>protected with lead</u> or other <u>radiation absorbing</u> materials.

Radiation sickness — well yes, it does all get a bit tiring...

<u>Marie Curie</u> discovered the <u>radioactive properties</u> of <u>radium</u> in 1898. Unfortunately, back then nobody knew that radioactivity was dangerous and she died of a <u>illness</u> caused by <u>exposure to radiation</u> in 1934.

Nuclear Fission

With a nuclear power station and some uranium you can generate a shed-load of energy.

Nuclear Fission — the Splitting Up of a Big Atomic Nucleus

1) A nuclear fission reaction is where an atomic nucleus (p.101) splits.
2) Nuclear fission reactions are useful because they release a lot of energy.

Nuclear Power Stations use Nuclear Fission

1) Nuclear power stations use the energy released from a nuclear fission reaction to heat water and turn it into steam.
2) The steam is used to turn a turbine, which is connected to a generator.
3) The generator generates electricity for use in homes and industries.
4) The "fuel" that's split is usually uranium-235 or plutonium-239 (or both).

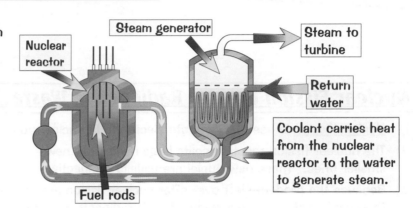

Nuclear reactor
Steam generator
Steam to turbine
Return water
Coolant carries heat from the nuclear reactor to the water to generate steam.
Fuel rods

The Chain Reaction:

1) For nuclear fission to happen, a slow moving neutron must be absorbed by a uranium or plutonium nucleus.
2) The neutron makes the nucleus unstable, causing it to split.
3) When a large atom splits in two it will form two new smaller nuclei.
4) Each time a uranium or plutonium nucleus splits up, it also spits out two or three neutrons.
5) One of the released neutrons might hit another nucleus, causing it to split too.
6) This causes a chain reaction — one reaction causes another reaction which causes another reaction...

Absorbed means 'taken into'.

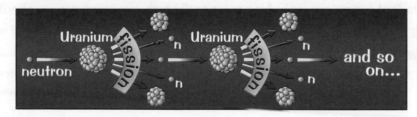

Uranium fission — n — Uranium fission — n — and so on...
neutron — n — n

Slow moving neutrons — brilliant at fission, terrible at sprinting...

Make sure you understand how the fission chain reaction works. The neutrons produced by the first fission go on to trigger other nuclei to split, and then they in turn chuck out more neutrons to trigger more reactions.

Nuclear Fission and Fusion

Just as you can split nuclei apart, you can _fuse_ them together too.

Nuclear Fusion — the Joining of Small Atomic Nuclei

1) Two <u>light nuclei</u> (such as hydrogen)
   can <u>join</u> to create a larger nucleus.

2) This is called <u>nuclear fusion</u>.

3) Fusion releases <u>a lot</u> of energy — all the energy
   released in <u>stars</u> comes from fusion (see next page).

4) Nuclear fusion reactions release <u>a lot more</u>
   energy than nuclear fission reactions.

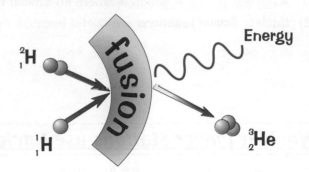

Nuclear Fission Creates Radioactive Waste...

1) <u>Nuclear fission</u> is used to generate electricity in nuclear power stations (see p.107).

2) The nuclear fission reaction splits large nuclei into new
   smaller ones. These new nuclei are usually <u>radioactive</u>.

3) Because the products left over after nuclear fission are <u>radioactive</u>,
   they can't just be thrown away. This is <u>radioactive waste</u>.

4) Radioactive waste is <u>difficult</u> and <u>expensive</u> to dispose of (get rid of) <u>safely</u>.

5) Nuclear <u>fuel</u> is <u>cheap</u> but the <u>overall cost</u> of nuclear power is <u>high</u>.

6) This is because it costs a lot of money to <u>set up the power plant</u> and make it <u>safe</u>.

7) Even more money is spent on final <u>decommissioning</u> (shutting it down) and <u>dealing with all the waste</u>.

8) Nuclear fission reactors also carry the risk of radiation <u>leaks</u> from the plant.

...So People are trying to Generate Electricity using Nuclear Fusion

1) Fusion <u>doesn't</u> leave behind a lot of radioactive <u>waste</u> and there's <u>plenty</u> of hydrogen for <u>fuel</u>.

2) The <u>big problem</u> is that fusion can only happen at <u>really high temperatures</u> — about <u>10 000 000 °C</u>.

3) The <u>temperatures</u> and <u>pressures</u> needed for fusion are too high to be able to do it in an ordinary container.

4) There are a few <u>experimental</u> reactors around, but none of them are generating electricity yet.

5) At the moment it takes <u>more power</u> to get up to the right temperature than the reactor can <u>produce</u>.

Ten million degrees — that's hot...

It'd be great if we could get nuclear fusion to work — there's a load of fuel available and it doesn't create much radioactive waste compared with fission. It's a shame that at the moment we need to use more energy to create the conditions for fusion than we can get out of it. Make sure you know the <u>pros</u> and <u>cons</u> of fission and fusion.

The Life Cycle of Stars

Stars go through <u>many stages</u> in their lives — just like teenagers.

1) Stars <u>form</u> from <u>clouds of DUST AND GAS</u>. The <u>force of gravity</u> makes the gas and dust <u>spiral in together</u> to form a <u>protostar</u>

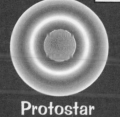

Protostar

2) The <u>gravitational forces</u> inside the star cause it to get <u>really hot</u>. When the temperature gets <u>high enough</u>, <u>hydrogen nuclei</u> undergo <u>nuclear fusion</u> to form <u>helium nuclei</u> (see p.108). This gives out massive amounts of <u>heat and light</u>. Smaller masses of gas and dust may also pull together to make <u>planets</u> that orbit the star.

Main Sequence Star

3) The star enters a <u>long stable period</u>. The <u>heat created</u> by the nuclear fusion provides an <u>outward pressure</u> to <u>balance</u> the <u>force of gravity</u> pulling everything <u>inwards</u>. The forces within the star are <u>balanced</u>. In this <u>stable</u> period it's called a <u>MAIN SEQUENCE STAR</u> and it lasts <u>several billion years</u>.

Stars much bigger than the Sun

Stars about the same size as the Sun

4) Eventually the <u>hydrogen</u> begins to <u>run out</u>. <u>Heavier elements</u> such as iron are made by nuclear fusion of <u>helium</u>. The star then <u>swells</u> into a <u>RED GIANT</u>, if it's a small star, or a <u>RED SUPER GIANT</u> if it's a big star. It becomes <u>red</u> because the surface <u>cools</u>.

Red Giant

White Dwarf

Black Dwarf

Red Super Giant

5) A <u>small-to-medium</u>-sized star like the Sun then becomes unstable. It <u>ejects</u> its <u>outer layer</u> of <u>dust and gas</u> — throwing it out into space.

6) This leaves behind a hot, dense solid core — a <u>WHITE DWARF</u>. Eventually this will cool down to a <u>BLACK DWARF</u> and finally disappear.

Supernova

Neutron Star...

...or Black Hole

7) <u>Big stars</u>, however, start to <u>glow brightly again</u> as they undergo more <u>fusion</u>. They form elements as <u>heavy as iron</u> in various <u>nuclear reactions</u>. Eventually they <u>explode</u> in a <u>SUPERNOVA</u>, forming elements <u>heavier than iron</u> and ejecting them into the universe to <u>form new planets and stars</u>.

8) The <u>exploding supernova</u> throws the outer layers of <u>dust and gas</u> into space, leaving a <u>very dense core</u> called a <u>NEUTRON STAR</u>. If the star is <u>big enough</u> this will become a <u>BLACK HOLE</u>.

Red Giants, White Dwarfs, Black Holes, Green Ghosts...

The early universe contained <u>only hydrogen</u>, the simplest and lightest element. It's only thanks to <u>nuclear fusion</u> inside stars that we have any of the other <u>elements</u> (apart from the ones that scientists make in the lab). Remember — the heaviest element produced in stable stars is <u>iron</u>, but it takes a <u>supernova</u> (or a lab) to create <u>the rest</u>.

Revision Summary for Physics 2b

...ne pretty heavy physics in this section. But just take it one page at a time and it's not so bad.
...ven allowed to go back through the pages for a sneaky peak if you get stuck on these questions.

1) What is the potential difference of the UK mains supply?

2) Sketch the oscilloscope trace that is produced by an a.c. electricity supply.

3) Give five examples of electrical dangers in the home.

4) Name the three wires in a three-core cable.

5) Sketch and label a properly wired three-pin plug.

6) Explain how a fuse and earth wire work together.

7) How does an RCCB stop you from getting electrocuted?

8)* Find the appropriate fuse (3 A, 5 A or 13 A) for these appliances:

   a) a toaster rated at 230 V, 1100 W,   b) an electric heater rated at 230 V, 2000 W.

9)* Calculate the power rating of a pair of hair straighteners that use 5400 J in 2 minutes.

10) Explain how the experiments of Rutherford and Marsden led to the nuclear model of the atom.

11) True or false: radioactive decay isn't random.

12) What is background radiation?

13) List two places where the level of background radiation is increased and explain why.

14) What type of particle is a beta particle?

15) Sketch the paths of an alpha particle and a beta particle travelling through a magnetic field.

16) What is half-life?

17) Give an example of how gamma radiation can be used in medicine.

18) Which is the most dangerous form of radiation if you eat it? Why?

19) Describe a safety measure you should take when handling radioactive sources.

20) Draw a diagram to show the fission of uranium-235. Explain how the chain reaction works.

21) What is nuclear fusion? Why is it difficult to make a working fusion reactor?

22) What is the main problem with generating electricity from nuclear power?

23) How are main sequence stars (like our Sun) formed?

24) Why will our Sun never form a black hole?

Using Equations

Sometimes in science you have to do some maths. Boo. Hiss.
But if you learn how to use equations, they're a great way to pick up marks in the exam.

Most of the Equations You Need Are Written in the Exam Paper

1) Equations can look tricky. But for all equations, all you
   have to do is times or divide one number by another.

2) It's really useful to know equations off by heart.

3) But most of the equations you need will be on
   an equation sheet in the exam paper. Hooray.

4) You just have to know which equation to use and how to use it.

equation sheet — exam paper

calculator

Example: A force of 200 N is used to move an object a distance of 5 m. How much work is done?

1) **Decide which equation to use and write it out.** → If you can't remember the equation to use, look for one on the equation sheet with force, distance and work done in it. → $W = F \times d$
   (W = work done, F = force, d = distance)

   $W = F \times d$

2) **Plug in the numbers.** Sometimes you'll need to get them in the right units first — see below. → Force (F) is 200 N, and distance (d) is 5 m. → $W = F \times d$
   $W = 200 \text{ N} \times 5 \text{ m}$

3) **Work out the answer with a calculator.** → → $W = 200 \text{ N} \times 5 \text{ m}$
   $= 1000$

4) **Don't forget the units.** → The units of work done are joules (J). → $W = 1000 \text{ J}$

Check Your Units

1) Before you plug the numbers in, check the numbers in the question have the right units.

2) You need to learn what the right units are for the things in the equations.

3) For example, distance always needs to be in metres (m) to use the work done equation.

4) If you're given a distance in centimetres, you have to change it to metres before you use the equation.

Another Example: Find the power, in W, of a hair drier that transfers 2 700 000 J of energy in 30 minutes.

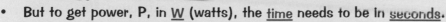

- Work out which equation you need to use: → $P = \dfrac{E}{t}$ (P = power, E = energy, t = time)
- The energy, E, is 2 700 000 J. The time, t, is 30 minutes.
- But to get power, P, in W (watts), the time needs to be in seconds.
- There are 60 seconds in a minute. So 30 minutes = $30 \times 60 = 1800 \text{ s}$.
- Now you can plug the numbers into the equation:
  $P = E \div t$
  $P = 2\,700\,000 \text{ J} \div 1800 \text{ s}$
  $P = 1500 \text{ W}$

5) Remember you always need to give the right units with your answer too.

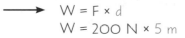

Index

Index

Index

Answers

Example on page 48

A is simple molecular, B is giant covalent,
C is giant ionic

Bottom of page 51

NaOH: 40, Fe_2O_3: 160, C_6H_{14}: 86

Bottom of page 52

a) 30.0% b) 88.9% c) 48.0%

Revision Summary for Chemistry 2a (page 55)

9) a) KCl   b) $CaCl_2$

10)

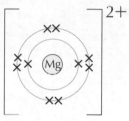

15) A: simple molecular, B: giant covalent,
C: giant ionic

19) a) 40 b) 108 c) 44 d) 84

21) a) 12.0% b) 27.3% c) 75.0%

Revision Summary for Chemistry 2b (page 70)

3)

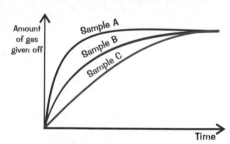

Revision Summary for Physics 2a (page 95)

4) $a = (v - u) \div t$
$a = (14 - 0) \div 0.4 = 35$ m/s^2

8) $F = ma$
$a = F \div m = 30 \div 4 = 7.5$ m/s^2

9) 120 N

13) Work done = force × distance.
$W = 535 \times 12 = 6420$ J

14) $E_p = m \times g \times h = 4 \times 10 \times 30 = 1200$ J

15) $E_k = \frac{1}{2} \times m \times v^2$
$E_k = \frac{1}{2} \times 78 \times 23^2 = 20\ 631$ J

16) $E_p = m \times g \times h = 78 \times 10 \times 20 = 15\ 600$ J
E_k gained = E_p lost = 15 600 J

25) $I = Q \div t$,
time = 1 minute = 1×60 = 60 seconds
$I = 240 \div 60 = 4$ A

29) $V = I \times R$
$V = 2 \times 0.6 = 1.2$ V

32) a) Current is the same everywhere in
the circuit and resistance adds up in a
series circuit.
Total resistance = 4 + 6 = 10 Ω

$I = V \div R = 12 \div 10 = 1.2$ A

b) Potential difference is shared between
the bulbs. $V = I \times R = 1.2 \times 6 = 7.2$ V

c) In parallel, the potential difference is
the same over each branch of the
circuit and is equal to the supply potential
difference, therefore the potential
difference over either bulb = 12 V.

Revision Summary for Physics 2b (page 110)

8) $P = I \times V$, $I = P \div V$
a) $I = 1100 \div 230 = 4.8$ A
so use a 5 A fuse.

b) $I = 2000 \div 230 = 8.7$ A
so use a 13 A fuse.

9) $P = E \div t$
time = 2 minutes = (2×60) = 120 s
$E = 5400$ J
$P = 5400 \div 120 = 45$ W